YOUR NONLEARNING CHILD

YOUR NONLEARNING CHILD

His World of Upside-Down

by Bert Kruger Smith , 1915-

WITH A PREFACE BY

Robert L. Sutherland, *Director*

THE HOGG FOUNDATION FOR MENTAL HEALTH

Beacon Press   BOSTON

The author gratefully acknowledges permission to quote from the following sources: *Childhood Aphasia and Brain Damage: A Definition,* edited by Sheldon Rappaport, published by Livingston Publishing Company, 1963, 1966; *The Birth of Language,* by Shulamith Kastein and Barbara Trace, published by Charles C Thomas, 1966; *Helping Children with Reading Disability,* by Ruth B. Edgington, Developmental Learning Materials, 1968; *Some Aspects of the Characteristics, Management and Education of the Child With Minimal Brain Dysfunction,* by Sam D. Clements, published by the Arkansas Association for Children with Learning Disabilities, Inc., and West Suburban Association for the Other Child, Inc. (Glen Ellyn, Illinois); "A Plan for Education," by Laura E. Lehtinen, in *Children with Minimal Brain Injury,* published by the National Society for Crippled Children and Adults, 1963; and *Discovering . . . Evaluating . . . Programming . . . for the Neurologically Handicapped Child,* by Charles R. Strother, published by the National Society for Crippled Children and Adults, 1963.

THIS BOOK IS DEDICATED, *with love, to the four generations of family members who have helped to keep my own world right-side up—mother, Fania Kruger; husband, Sid; children and their mates, Randye and Gordon Beavers, Sheldon and Linda; and their sons, Stacy and Russell.*

ACKNOWLEDGMENTS

AN AUTHOR can acknowledge the assistance of persons whose aid is chronicled in letters or manuscript suggestions. However, it is not possible to pinpoint the help of the numerous persons who were encouraging and supportive in subtle ways. They are hereby thanked.

Dr. Robert L. Sutherland, Director of The Hogg Foundation, has made possible the writing of this book. Both personally and as representative of the Foundation, he has encouraged and aided my visiting of facilities and taking time to work on the manuscript. I am truly grateful.

Dr. Darrel Mase, Dean of Health Related Services, University of Florida, served as an ideal critic reader. He read the manuscript painstakingly on two levels—for content and accuracy and for style. I owe him much. I appreciate also the continuous interest and support of personnel from Southwest Medical School in Dallas, The University of Texas Medical Branch in Galveston, and The University of Texas at Austin. Dr. Robert L. Stubblefield, Chairman of the Department of Psychiatry, Southwest Medical School, read the entire manuscript and gave me the benefit of his knowledge, as did Dr. Robert Strong and Dr. Jerry Hasterok, assistant professors of special education, The University of Texas at Austin. My appreciation goes out to all of them. Dr. Lear Ashmore, associate professor of speech, and Dr. Ralph Hanna, assistant professor of special education, both of The University of Texas at Austin, were two of the people who went far beyond the second mile in reading and making suggestions.

Dr. Ray Barsch, professor of special education, Southern Connecticut State College, was extremely helpful with specific information, as was Dr. Corrine Kass, Coordinator of Interrelated Areas and Learning Disorders, U.S. Office of Education. Dr. Orie Forbis, Director of the Austin Child Guidance Center, aided with suggestions. Others who made particular efforts to obtain and share material were Merwin G. Beavers, Sr., Lee Wright, and Murry Dwayne Thompson. Miss Jean Pearce, a teacher, served as a conscientious reader. Dr. James Turman, Executive Director of the Texas Youth Council, Dr. Lucius Waites, pediatric neurologist at the Texas Scottish Rite Hospital, and Dr. Jack Boston, private psychiatrist, helped give me introductory insights into the problems.

Many busy and involved persons took hours or days from their schedules to help me discover all that I could about children with special problems in learning.

At The Pathway School in Jeffersonville, Pennsylvania, Dr. Sheldon Rappaport gave me a complete panoramic view of the program for brain-injured children. I thank him and his wife, Florence, as well as Dr. William Adamson, psychiatric consultant to The Pathway School, who spent much time in orienting me to specific problems. Appreciation is given also for the help of numerous staff members, each of whom was friendly and warmly interested.

The Menninger Foundation is without parallel. To list names here is an act of omission, for every person with whom I came in contact went out of his way to give help. Dr. Robert E. Switzer, Director of the Children's Division, began it all with an invitation to visit the Menninger Foundation. He scheduled and planned the visit, with help from his associates. Particular appreciation is expressed to Dr. J. Cotter Hirschberg, Director of Training in Child Psychiatry, and Dr. Clyde L. Rousey, psychologist, Dr. Phillip Rennick, Dr. Dorothy

Fuller, Dr. M. Ack, Dr. J. Tarlton Morrow, Jr., Miss Jane Baxter, Mr. Randy Schmidt, and Mr. Arthur Mandelbaum, Chief Social Worker. Mrs. Cay Menninger deserves special acknowledgment for her personal aid.

Dr. Tina Bangs and her associates at the Houston Speech and Hearing Center were most helpful.

All members of The Hogg Foundation staff were of aid in various ways. Specific appreciation is extended to Mrs. Elaine Zinn, whose typing of the manuscript was an invaluable help and to Mrs. Lois Jeane Davis who served in checking sources and references. Dr. Bernice Milburn Moore, Mr. David J. Latz, Mrs. Etelka S. Lynn, Mrs. Lucille Wilson, Mrs. Jean Friday, and all other members of The Hogg Foundation staff were helpful in numerous ways. Dr. Ira Iscoe, Hogg Foundation consultant, aided on numerous occasions.

To those families and individuals whose names are not used but whose difficult experiences were shared goes my special gratitude.

Family assistance—support, encouragement, and interest —is vital. Appreciation is expressed to my mother and my husband, who read each word of the manuscript and gave suggestions, and to Shel and Linda and Randye and Gordon, whose pride and delight made the task pleasant.

BERT KRUGER SMITH

CONTENTS

PREFACE

By Robert L. Sutherland, *Director*

THE HOGG FOUNDATION FOR MENTAL HEALTH

THE BAFFLING, subtle, and amorphous quality of a learning disability in a child may prove frustrating to the youngster, aggravating to the teacher, and guilt-producing to the parent. Unrecognized, it can enlarge into emotional disturbance in the young person.

The child for whom there is no "model of competence" by which to measure himself may feel only that something is wrong, that he fails where others succeed. His teacher may be thrown offstride by his hyperactivity or failure to learn.

The parents' gradual or sudden awareness of the difficulty may catch them off balance also. They may still be preoccupied with their jobs, with world conditions, or with the needs of their other children when they feel the weight of this new problem. Their response may take various forms. A common one is a quick sense of their own guilt. Another is a covert feeling of resentment and injustice tinged with a measure of impatience.

A learning difficulty in a child looms large because our culture places much importance on communication, both written and oral, and also on the acquisition of knowledge. Indispensable schooling is based on it. So is socializing with peer groups. And likewise, the prospect of career success is affected.

Basic knowledge about human nature is surprisingly widespread, thanks to modern research and the skillful writers who translate it for the use of mass media. Bert Kruger Smith is one of the best of them. She postponed for ten years her efforts to communicate scientific material in terms useful to parents.

She wanted first to become familiar with the ways and limitations of research and clinical practice in this area. She also learned about the fallacy of oversimplification.

Within the setting of The Hogg Foundation for Mental Health, she found a sympathetic climate in which to work. Since its inception, the Hogg Foundation's concern has centered on the mental health of persons of all ages and on prevention and early intervention efforts. As a member of the professional staff, Mrs. Smith made numerous pamphlet excursions into the field of parent-child understanding before tackling, in 1964, the full-length book entitled *No Language But A Cry*.

Parents, teachers, fellow-writers, and research workers themselves found the summaries in her book so sound and at the same time so clear and interesting that her publishers urged her to do a companion volume. *Your Nonlearning Child* is the result.

Prior to writing each book, Mrs. Smith visited centers which specialized in work with children. She invited as critic readers persons who are expert in the area. She read primary sources and attended seminars.

The current volume will be of value to teachers and to new workers in the various professions. It will be useful to the volunteers who are beginning to work with children, their own or other persons'. Parents who read the book will not be tempted to invent problems in their children. However, if problems exist, mothers and fathers will be provided knowledge and guide signs to the sources of help. This volume will help offset feelings of futility, indecision, and guilt.

This book does not gloss over the difficulties faced by certain children, and what child does not have some problems? However, it always points the way to finding help and to stressing the positive abilities of every child.

YOUR NONLEARNING CHILD

CHAPTER I

THE NONLEARNING CHILD
"I Am a Watermelon"

STAND ON YOUR HEAD. The world is strange and unpredictable. Ceiling at your feet. Rug at your head. Chairs and tables with no useful function. For you the world is upside down, and nothing in it makes order or brings meaning.

Or you are in a play. You move to center stage—and forget your lines. Instead of receiving your cue from the wing, you hear a dozen voices from right and left, from above and below. You turn in confusion and then in panic, trying to respond to the proper note.

You can read short sentences, long ones. Paragraphs and pages. But it is like repeating foreign words you don't understand. You pronounce the words and say the phrases, but no meaning comes from them.

Children with learning disabilities spend their days in a world which seems to be tilted or reversed or wholly upside down. They have no rule book for living because they cannot perceive the world in an organized way. The disabilities may range from mild problems of reading or computing figures to severe disorders which affect every area of their lives.

A famous singer who had been going gradually deaf awoke from her ear surgery in a state of rage at the grating sound of a pile of stone being hauled across a gravel yard. But what she heard, in reality, was a hand moving across the sheets of her bed. Her mind had accommodated to the lack of hearing and now had to become accustomed again to the perception of sounds as they were. One's world is ordered by what he learns and how he learns and adapts to it.

3

Some children with learning problems, it is believed, may have undeveloped or underdeveloped pathways in the brain. This dysfunction in the brain is sometimes difficult to detect by scientific tests and sometimes can be recognized only through the behavior it causes. Many such children have difficulty in retaining what they hear, others what they see; some can hear and see satisfactorily but cannot put experiences into a meaningful whole.

Learning disabilities. Minimal brain dysfunction. Cognitive perceptual motor deficits. Brain damage. Dyslexia. All of these labels describe some of the children; none of them encompasses all of them.

Children who have severe learning disabilities are not "neat" in their disorders. They cannot be boxed into label or method. Rather, like chameleons, they change color and move from one category to another. Timmy, at 9, may be able to work math problems above his grade level but cannot read his name. Jane speaks with fluency but is unable to write a sentence. And Mark can take down any dictation but will not know how to read a word of it.

These baffling, subtle, and strange disabilities—what causes them? The answers are as complex and as difficult to catalog as the children.

Learning disabilities are universal, experienced by every individual. Most people, called upon to function in their areas of "dysfunction" rather than of competence, would fail totally. The ballerina might be a miserable accountant; the golf pro would make a poor editor; the business executive would come in last in a swimming meet.

Everyone has learning disabilities, greater in some areas than in others. Also, everyone learns at a different pace and in a different way. Children's growth and development are often uneven and unpredictable. But it is vital to the life of a child that parents and teachers know what is "immaturity" of learning or "developmental lag" and what is a dysfunction in some area of his brain.

We shall look at the whole spectrum of learning disabilities but shall be concerned most with those which are severe enough to stymie, divert, stunt, or inhibit children from reaching their full life potentials.

† † †

At another time and in another culture learning disabilities did not carry the weight that they do today. In rural America it was possible for a boy or girl to learn the manual skills which would keep him productive without knowing how to read or compute figures or even write.

When the sweet smell of honeysuckle hung heavy above the farmhouse and the husband and wife sat together on the porch swing, quietly recounting the day's activities, they could feel useful and successful without having the complex knowledge of computation or writing. A youngster who did not do well in school could begin to spend full-time on the farm. And if he developed knowledge of how to plant and when to reap, if he helped with the slaughtering and the curing, and if he were willing and useful, he became an important member in the community. So did the young woman who could can and cook and sew and tend the sick.

But in today's culture no one can escape the need to read and comprehend. There is scarcely a task which does not call on such abilities. No friendly butcher will explain each cut of meat; no grocer will help to compute amounts of food and comparative costs. A person cannot take a bus without knowing how to read the signs, nor can he walk safely without being able to interpret the notices posted on many corners. He cannot use most products without comprehending instructions.

Certainly he cannot drive a car safely without such knowledge. And few people are able to obtain any kind of job, except the most menial, without an education.

Thus, the child with learning disabilities is penalized by his own lacks and by the culture within which he lives. His very life, physically and psychologically, is dependent on his being able to conform at least to the minimum norms set out by the world into which he was born.

What are some of the skills he needs?

Perception

Perception, a simple word, connotes the entire scope and range of a world. Each person is concerned about how certain people see him; each of his acts depends on his own insight concerning that move. Even with relatively intact systems of operation, every individual may have difficulty with some types of observation. However, generally, there are overall perceptions which form common bases for action among people.

Imagine, then, what it must be like for the child with serious learning disabilities to perceive differently from anyone else and to have difficulty with even the simplest types of acts.

The problem is stated in this way by Dr. Newell C. Kephart:

> One of the initial learning problems of the child is that of becoming familiar with the basic realities of the universe which surrounds him. Essentially, these basic realities are two— space and time. . . . The great majority of brain-injured children have difficulty in making the adequate observations necessary to the development of a space-time structure and even more difficulty in organizing these observations into a comprehensive schema.[1]

[1] Newell C. Kephart, "The Needs of Teachers for Specialized Information on Perception," in *The Teacher of Brain-Injured Children*, William M. Cruickshank, ed., New York: Syracuse University Press, 1966, p. 171.

The infant, according to Jean Piaget, the Swiss psychologist noted for his studies of learning in children, first finds out about force by manipulating something heavy or pushing against some very large and unmoving object. Other knowledge comes to him through his various senses. He learns about roundness when he sees and touches a ball, thus coordinating his sense of touch with his eye "cues."

This business of perception begins almost at birth. Arnold Gesell, for many years director of the Institute of Child Development, in some of his studies discovered that even premature infants, when they are first born, can track bright lights.

Moving into three-dimensional space, one needs the added facility of auditory perception. Or, as Bryant J. Cratty points out, "The sound of the ball hitting the catcher's mitt permits the pitcher to make better judgments of speed when paired with a visual impression of the ball's movement toward the plate. Sounds help us localize objects in space and provide important cues in forming perceptions of reality."[2]

The ability to perceive, thus, is vital to anyone in organizing his world and in learning to function in some orderly way within it.

The process of visualizing the world requires numerous skills which must develop as the child grows. For example, in order to perceive space in three dimensions, the eyes must converge upon a single object. As explained by Bryant Cratty:

The space field is rarely a stable one. Movements of objects within two and three planes continually occur to influence perceptual judgments. . . . The athlete continually bases his actions upon perception of dynamic qualities in space: of balls coming toward him to be caught, hit, batted, or struck or of runners moving away from him. . . . The picture is further

[2] Bryant J. Cratty, *Movement Behavior and Motor Learning,* Philadelphia: Lee and Febiger, 1964, p. 284.

complicated when it is considered that usually more than one object is in motion within the real world.[3]

Dr. Cratty then makes it clear that the time dimension must be considered when one thinks of perception of movement in two-dimensional and three-dimensional space. Thus, the delicate interweaving of skills, one relating to another, one dependent on another, one following another—all of these relate to the way in which a child is able to perceive his world and make of it a reality with which he can live in some meaningful fashion.

Thought Development

How does the thought process itself develop? What are the guidelines by which children are able to locate the paths to learning? The stages in thought development are said by many experts to be threefold. First is a lack of differentiation between self and the world. The infant, for example, considers the world as an extension of himself and his mother as the "need filler" for his own wants. During the second stage he perceives the world as different from and outside of him. The young child begins to sort out his world in terms of his own body, then his own belongings, and finally those items outside of his possessions. Finally, there comes the conceptual stage when symbols represent objects in the world and the world is known in terms of abstract representations.

Another aspect of differentiation is that thought, or internal mental action, generally helps the individual to organize himself and often to delay action until it is appropriate. The child with learning disabilities has no such "brake" to keep him from acting immediately upon any impulse which triggers him.

[3] *Ibid.,* p. 123.

To have full language capacity the child must achieve verbal comprehension, expression, concept formation, visual memory and association, and ability to calculate. As the child learns to use his language, he first listens and then speaks. Reading comes next and then writing. The sequence is natural and easy for most young people, but for some the gate of comprehension is slammed shut before their faces.

Language

For a child with damage the art of speaking may be a most difficult barrier. In *The Birth of Language* the authors say, "It is only when language fails to develop that we realize what a complex process it is and what intricate patterns of integration within the nervous system have to be established to allow verbal communication to emerge. The child so affected may then show not only impairment in language and speech but impairment in other aspects of his development."[4] It is pointed out that many children who later in their school careers have reading problems were also those who in their young years suffered from language difficulties.

For other children, speaking may be natural and spontaneous, while the art of reading may prove to be awesome and complex. A number of skills must be developed for the child to learn to read, and many added ones are needed for the comprehension and interpretation of what is read.

Yet some children with learning disabilities compensate in ways that keep other people from knowing that they have a problem. One young woman with a reading disorder was able to enter graduate school by dint of spending hours in reading what might take minutes for someone else. Motivation can be a powerful force in overcoming many disorders. Helen Keller,

[4] Shulamith Kastein and Barbara Trace, *The Birth of Language,* Springfield, Illinois: Charles C Thomas, 1966, p. 5.

without being able to see or to hear, was able to learn, once
the breakthrough was made, to give pattern to her life.

Causation

Why do some children have problems with perception, thought
development, and language? Here controversy ranges from
those who note observable brain damage in learning disorders
to those who speak of "faulty wiring" or some minimal dysfunction in some area of the brain. Many explanations are
given for this less obvious dysfunction. Some physicians think
that it may not be brain damage but a biological and congeni-
tal disturbance in the organizational patterns of the central
nervous system. It has been estimated that about 10 per cent
of all the children in school have reading or learning disabilities as major problems.

In addition to recognizing the physical base of learning
disorders, some people feel that such disabilities may be the
result of neurotic or psychotic disorders or simply poor teaching. The neurotic problems may come from lack of identification. For example, many children from poverty areas have
never had the opportunity to learn through the simple acts
of communication with other people, through the sharing of
knowledge, or through the following of example. Early feeding problems may be another source for neurotic disorders.
One psychologist has stated that a child who has been fed
forcefully can reject learning. Or a child who has battled with
his parents concerning toilet training may be able, as he grows
older, to displace the fight to something else. Another example
is the child who refuses to learn because of sexual inhibitions.
His own questions concerning sex remain unanswered; thus,
he does not learn to answer questions. Or, children may refuse
to learn because of their own guilt feelings about their thoughts
or fantasies. They ask to be punished for not conforming to
the learning pattern, and in being punished, are relieved of

their guilt. Or, a child may not be able to learn because there is some dreadful secret in his family which he longs to understand but which he is not helped to know. One little boy whose father was desperately ill was sent to a clinic because he was unable to learn in school. Once in the therapist's office he was invited to play with some hand puppets. The little boy placed a puppet in each hand, one representing the father and another the son. The boy puppet said, "I want to know." And the father puppet sternly answered, "You know enough!"

The neurotic nonlearner probably lacks aggression and aggression is needed to learn. We try to "devour a book," or "dig a subject." Occasionally children are so inhibited in their aggressive qualities that they have equal difficulty in the acquisition of learning.

While the neurotic and psychotic disorders have come to the attention of the public in past years, the more subtle types of learning disabilities are only now taking their full place in the spectrum of concerns of scientists, teachers, and parents. Some children have normal or above normal IQ's. They do not demonstrate abnormalities on an electroencephalogram. There is no obvious social or emotional problem which keeps them from learning. Yet they are "uneven" in their patterns of learning and have serious problems in some areas. They seem to be unable to learn certain skills through regular methods of instruction. Their behavior demonstrates the possibility of brain dysfunction. They have impairments in one or more of the following areas: perceptual, conceptual, psychomotor and motor, language, memory, and emotional control.

Who are these children with learning disabilities? How did they acquire their difficulties?

One may be John, a blue-eyed infant placidly discovering the taste of his toes and the feel of his baby fist in his mouth. Johnny, seeing the world of sunshine against the patterned wallpaper above his crib, marking his days by the contentment of his body and the smiles of his parents. When the plague of meningitis hit Johnny with a fever above 106, he became then a tiny body of pain. For forty-eight hours he battled death as his parents and doctors wrapped him in steaming mustard plaster towels to open his pores and let some of the body heat escape. His blue eyes turned white; his body became flaccid.

The crisis passed. Johnny lived, and all was well until he began school. Suddenly it was discovered that John could not read, could not comprehend written language, and could not learn to write. After exhaustive tests, Johnny's brain damage was pinpointed; he was put into a specialized remedial reading program. Also, he spent half of his days in classes for brain-injured children, and eventually evolved into an achieving young person who is competent in sports and classroom learning. However, Johnny had to have special permission to waive his foreign language requirements. Spanish was beyond his area of ability.

Or there was Kim, six and solid. A youngster who enjoyed his body and who used it every waking moment. He ran when he could walk; he wrestled with his peers; he jumped fences, turned handsprings. If he didn't get hungry, ravenously, his mother might never have been able to bring him into the house to wash his freckled face and hands.

It was Kim's competitive eagerness which sent him running into the street after a ball. No truckdriver can halt a huge vehicle in a few feet. Kim lay splattered on the pavement. Everyone thought him dead, and, for some months afterward, they wondered if it might not have been better if he were. For Kim suffered massive brain damage and lay in a coma for many weeks. When, finally, he began to see the world, it was as an infant might. He had lost his competence for speech and for the simplest of motor activities.

Kim required years of patient work to bring him self-help skills, basic reading, slow movement.

One can understand learning disorders in John and Kim. But these two boys are only a small fraction of the population of children whose problems cripple them in one way or another. The subtlety of some disturbances confuses parents and often keeps them from seeking or finding competent help until the child has acquired an overlay of emotional disturbance added to his other problems.

Let us see some of the children who exhibit learning difficulties without, at the same time, showing obvious brain damage.

Marty has never done well in school, although his mother and father are college graduates and he has been exposed to literature at home. In his preschool years there were few problems. Marty and the two boys next door had romped together, taken swimming lessons, used each others' backyard swings. Life had presented no unusual difficulties until Marty came to school.

There he was faced with a new set of problems. His most important job at school was to learn to understand and produce written symbols. Now he stood against a wall which was taller than he was. Although Marty could speak with ease and could understand what was said to him, he could not transfer that knowledge from oral to written presentation without laborious and lengthy effort.

At the same time that the written problem became evident, Marty's other incompetencies were noted. He could do well at sports, but he was uncertain and slow in writing or drawing, in tasks which required "fine" motor coordination using small muscles and combinations of skills.

Although Marty's IQ tested in the superior range, he seemed unable to complete a task of writing or drawing unless he was constantly supervised or prodded. His distractibility kept him far behind the other children in his class.

For Marty the answer came in hiring a tutor, in putting

him into a smaller class, and in giving him the painstaking attention which he needed to learn the laborious task of reading well.

What happened to Marty to make him a scholastic problem? No one quite knows. There was a bit of history of "breath-holding spells" when he was an infant, spells during which he became stiff and lost consciousness for a few seconds; no head injury had occurred. Also in the family, numerous people, including Marty's father, had reading and other scholastic difficulties.

Finally, let us look at Polly, whose early history does not even contain the clues of breath-holding, of possible convulsive disorders. Polly grew up in a family of achievers. Her older brother was the school's delight, her younger a consistent scholar.

Polly's brown eyes and auburn hair often made strangers stop to note her. Her smile was instantaneous and contagious. Polly was irresistible. She identified with her father, who was a physician, and made plans from little-girl days to be a doctor too.

But school not only halted Polly's ambition, it also erased her smile and replaced it with two small frown wrinkles, like birds' wings between her eyes. While her younger brother caught up with and passed her, Polly labored with her reading skills, with her math problems, and with her writing.

Only Polly's mother knew of the constant struggle made by the brown-eyed girl. For it was Polly's mother who sat up with her at night and painstakingly taught her spelling, word by word, and who helped her read, slow sentence by slower sentence. They worked until Polly knew her lesson perfectly. And then in the morning, it was gone, all of it, as if it had been put upon a blackboard which had been erased during the night.

Because the family was prominent, Polly was promoted from grade to grade and finally, by dint of taking vocational courses, stood on the high school platform where her mother and father and brother had been before her and received her diploma. But she did not join her older brother in medical school nor her younger brother at the university. Instead, Polly threw herself into volunteer work and gave of her personal skills to youngsters on the children's wards of the local hospital.

Why Marty and Polly were as they were no one really knows. Some brain dysfunction should be inferred from behavior, since it sometimes cannot be "seen" on an electroencephalogram. Normal tests do not rule out the possibility. In cases like Marty's, it is true that often several people in the family have exhibited similar problems. The behavioral symptoms are much like those of adults who have had brain injury. However, there are two important differences. One is that the child may show no observable physical signs of brain damage, and the other is that the child's problem of "recovery" is different. For just like the seriously emotionally disturbed child, the one with learning difficulties has no competences to which to return, no memory of success, no guidelines to direct him.

The one fact which emerges from all of this discussion of learning disabilities is that there is no one entity. Combinations of learning problems are as numerous as the children who evidence them, and the solutions must be individualized.

Viewing a class of first-grade pupils, one sees scrawny little boys with uneven teeth, small girls in blues and pinks giggling together, a pudgy youngster running his fingers through the many cowlicks in his hair as he traces a line. An earnest girl licks her lips and mouths words as she tries to read a sentence.

They look young and new and very uncomplicated. Although in some children learning disabilities can be diagnosed in infancy and early childhood, within such a class often come the first real evidences of learning disabilities. We have seen Johnny, Kim, Marty, and Polly. Let us see one more child, whose difficulties were so great that her family brought her to the Menninger Clinic in Topeka for diagnosis and possibly treatment.

Alice looked like a youngster who should be holding tea parties in her backyard or skipping from school in the afternoon with her arms around her chum. Alice resembled a fine Dresden figure—with glasses. Her golden hair hung long, and her skin was translucent.

How did a pretty little girl become a failure in her own eyes by the age of eight? Her story differs from the four young people described, though her difficulties were much the same. She could not read, and seemingly, could not be taught. She seemed unable to do anything correctly in spelling or math, and her sense of failure was making her withdrawn and quietly unhappy.

The thought of her having to repeat the second grade brought her parents and her to the Menninger Clinic for evaluation. The questions raised: Was the child brain-damaged? Was she retarded? Was she emotionally disturbed?

Alice and her parents moved into Topeka, Kansas, and the painstaking unraveling of the learning problem began. For ten days the trio stayed together while Alice underwent a battery of tests and spent a great deal of time with various specialists in child psychology, psychiatry, and speech pathology. Meanwhile, her parents talked with the social worker assigned to the case.

The team met at the end of the first three days to decide what steps to take next. At the end of the ten-day period, in a quiet room overlooking rolling lawns and spring-green shrubs, a dozen top professionals and a trio of fellows-in-training spent the entire morning trying to fathom the riddle of why Alice didn't learn.

Constant interweaving, like the shuttle of a loom, went through the discussion. When the neurologist stated that Alice wore a watch but could not tell time, the child psychiatrist said that after Alice had been in her office for a time and had grown confident of her relationship with the physician, the doctor had drawn a watch on a piece of paper. Alice had then been able to tell time by hours and by minutes.

Obviously Alice was very frightened to show what she knew. Why? During numerous tests Alice had demonstrated at least average ability; there was no observable brain damage; she was even able to correct mistakes made by her interviewer when she was confident of her relationship with him.

Because of the many "views" of Alice and her parents, the team was able to add to, subtract from, or correct impressions and observations made by others.

Essentially, the findings were these: Alice's father had undergone serious abdominal surgery when Alice was a few years old. The illness had left him frail and tenuously holding to life. The family had kept from Alice discussion of the difficulty and its possible consequences so that all that Alice knew was that there was some ominous secret within her household.

Why should she be helpless, ineffectual, unaware, gullible, and failing in school? What lay behind her disappointments and frustrations? How could she be helped, the team wondered.

As the constant interplay and interaction continued, a picture began to appear of a little girl who had to keep herself out of the path of thoughts which frightened her, such as the death of her parents. She was able to protect herself with neurotic tics and fantasies.

What were the secondary gains, the staff asked, that Alice achieved by not learning and by having a great number of illnesses? She punished herself by her nonachievement, but also she took herself out of the competitive market.

Alice's parents were a loving couple but were also people whose fears about health, their own and Alice's, kept them constantly "over" her. By not learning, Alice achieved a secondary gain, that of having her mother take care of her.

The parents, through their own fears and needs, kept Alice dependent, and Alice was unable to rebel or show aggression toward her parents. Here, then, she was caught in a double bind. School encouraged questions. Alice's parents rejected her questions about the items which were of greatest importance to her, her father's health.

What brought the parents to the point of having diagnostic study for Alice was Alice's having chosen the most damaging symptoms possible for her disturbance—nonlearning. Thus, the circular needs of parents and child became the subject for discussion. Could the parents become free? And could they "free" Alice? Could they give her "permission" to have therapy on a steady basis? Could they be helped to stop giving her contradictory signals, such as "Stay little and dependent but do well in school"?

The social worker, who said, "Let me speak for the parents," told of their anxieties and discomforts regarding Alice, while the team who had worked with the child observed her miseries and discomfort.

The recommendation for Alice and her parents was that she be taken to a city near her home once a week for psychotherapy in order that she could begin to release herself from her multiple fears regarding her parents and herself and could have the freedom to learn.

In the case of Alice, neurotic forces were at work to hold

the child back from learning and growing in intellectual strength. Tedious unraveling of family patterns was necessary before Alice's problems could be revealed.

Johnny had had encephalitis. Kim was hit by a truck. Marty had some slight history of breath-holding and unconsciousness which may have been the subtle factors that kept him from learning. Polly could not read, but there were no obvious clues concerning her disability. And Alice failed in school because of delicate and unhealthy internal functioning within her own family.

And these are only five of thousands of children who exhibit learning disabilities in one degree or another. The first-grade class with its clusters of earnest little boys and girls around the child-sized tables may contain a variety of individual problem areas. Let us look at two other kinds of "non-learners," the culturally deprived and the mentally ill.

Walk to the round table where the slow readers are. Their group may be called the "Bluebirds," but all of the children know that the smart kids are in the "Redbird" group and the medium ones in the "Robin" group. These children labor over the first-grade readers. The ability to translate written word to thought escapes them in some degree or another. Maybe Johnny, Kim, Marty, Polly, and Alice or their counterparts sit here. In addition, there may be Steve, whose mother worked half the night, leaving Steve and his brothers and sisters to fend for themselves. Steve may have trouble learning because such learning has not been a part of his environment from babyhood. He grew up in a little shack on the other side of the creek. He has more brothers and sisters and half-brothers and half-sisters than he can name. Steve has never known the simple act of talking with another person. His life has been a series of two-word sentences, uttered angrily by his mother as she returned from a long day at work or as she prepared to

leave for one. "Sit down." "Shut up." "Go out." Holding a conversation was unknown to Steve. So was the joy of discovery.
Steve is already behind before he enters the first grade. All of
the plastic, eager years of learning what life is about have been
lost to him and may never be regained.

One study financed by the National Institute for Mental
Health reported that from age 15 months to 18 months, the
IQ's of children from culturally deprived neighborhoods and
those from more advantaged ones showed no differences. However, after 18 months, the children from the deprived areas
began to lose ground, as their IQ scores diminished.[5] And Dr.
Ralph Rabinovitch has noted that children from culturally
deprived homes, coming into special education programs in increasing numbers, evidence the same symptoms as do the children who have some kind of minimal brain dysfunction or
mental retardation.

Finally, among the nonlearners is the population of seriously emotionally disturbed children. They speak through their
behavior. The withdrawal, the hyperactivity, the lack of ability to tolerate a learning situation may all be evidences of
serious disturbance, an acid eating into the fabric of childhood. Many of these children, too, have normal or above
normal intelligence. But their "block" is emotional, and the
ability to learn will return to them only as they gain the
ability to live in the world again.

Some of these young people have been immobilized by
panic or by fear when faced with a test of their learning. For
example, Marcy, who became seriously ill her first year in
college, describes her reactions to tests as one of absolute
panic. "I could know the material perfectly," she says, "and
would have a complete blackout when the test was put before
me."

Looking at the half dozen children described, one can see why no one label or cause can be pinned on the youngsters who have learning disabilities. Not only are the problems different in scope, kind, and duration, but the causes are just as varied.

If, then, the children differ and the symptoms differ, it stands to reason that the treatments must differ also. The great danger, according to the experts, is to remember the label and forget the child. For each of the children with learning disabilities is a child with special needs and hopes and desires for achievement.

A child who has few if any "success" experiences uses negative behavior as his only means of "attack." Such a child may have impairment in his thinking abilities, dysfunction in memory retention and recall, paralyzing fears, refusal to participate in group activities, and—most vital—lack of confidence in his ability to learn. This lack of confidence becomes a circular reaction, which makes the child continue in his noncompetitive methods of nonlearning.

Before any diagnosis is made of a child's disability, a careful examination must be given to determine if basic abilities are intact. The child's general health pattern must be studied minutely, along with his hearing, sight, and motor abilities. For instance, a child who performed in the same manner as one with serious learning disorders was found to have hypoglycemia, a disease in which his blood sugar was used too rapidly and forcefully, causing him to be hyperactive and distractable.

After such an examination is made and after it is determined that the child is able to receive signals through his sensory organs, then it can be determined that it is in his brain that the message is not being decoded or routed in proper fashion. Mechanically the child may be in perfect shape, but he is like a high-powered car in tiptop condition with a driver who does not know how to start, stop, or direct the movement of the automobile.

The area of learning disorders, like the wind in a storm, seems to move in numerous directions. A great deal of thoughtful effort has been given to the problem of definition. For instance, Dr. J. Cotter Hirschberg, psychiatrist and associate director of the children's service of the Menninger Foundation,[6] makes it clear, as do others, that the area of learning disabilities is large and complex and should demand a broad approach. There must not be an either/or frame of reference but rather a number of interrelated factors. The five items mentioned by Dr. Hirschberg as being involved in consideration of learning disabilities are:

1. *Psychological factors.* a) Disturbances in visual, auditory, and kinesthetic sensation. b) Problems of perception and memory. Learning is a complex mental activity which involves several areas of brain functioning all working together. It poses a system problem involving analytic and synthetic processes. The child has to learn to recognize letters and combinations. He has to take combinations and associate them with sounds. He has to apply meaning to the letter combinations.
2. *Actual brain damage which affects psychological factors in learning.* Some children with learning disorders have an aphasic problem.
3. *Sociological factors.* The child with early deprivation and limited social experience of a rewarding kind may have a learning disability.
4. *Motivational factors.* Motivations for learning in either the family or the child are significant.
5. *Emotional factors.* These are very difficult to sort out.

[6] Personal interview, May 1967.

We know that learning disability produces an emotional problem and that emotional factor can produce a learning disability. These facts must be taken into account: a) There is no single personality type. No single conflict is always involved. b) A general learning problem can also include a reading problem. A general problem in learning is obscured by a disability to read. c) There may be difficulty in handling aggression. Excessive amounts of guilt or excessive anxieties can cause these problems. These anxieties may be around hostile or destructive impulses or fantasies. d) Most of these children will show disturbance in ego development. Some functions are advanced and some far too infantile. Usually there are faulty identification patterns. e) There will be anxiety about curiosity. Sometimes the parents have placed a barrier on curiosity. f) There is a real struggle over secondary gains. Staying out of school may have special meaning for the child and mother. Some gains are to be had from helplessness. There is wish for an effortless reward, as "If you really loved me, you wouldn't force me to learn." g) There is lack of orderly progression in the child's learning around reality testing. The parents have not made clear what demands are made and what the consequences may be. The child does not get an increasing sense of reality testing.

When working in the area of learning disabilities, says Dr. Hirschberg, these three factors must be taken into account: 1) The necessity to recognize the complexity of the problem; 2) the necessity to understand fully the nature of the problem before instituting help; and 3) the necessity to know the real value of beginning early. What happens to a child's group of sequences in learning may be damaged by the time he is of school age.

In 1966 a national effort was begun to set out criteria for diagnosis and treatment. A three-phase research project was set up through the joint efforts of the National Institute of Neurological Diseases and Blindness, Public Health Service, and the Easter Seal Research Foundation of the National Society for Crippled Children and Adults.

One of the reports lists four possible reasons for the rise in number of "children with minimal brain dysfunction": 1) The increased refinement in diagnostic techniques and skills over the last several years; 2) the growing necessity for more precise classification of the learning and behavioral disorders of children; 3) an apparent increase in the number of children compromised by neurologic dysfunctions; and 4) a growing dissatisfaction expressed by many medical workers concerning purely psychogenic and interpersonal explanations for any disorganized or poorly understood behavior.

After reviewing the concepts of organicity versus environment, the report concluded that: "We cannot afford the luxury of waiting until causes can be unquestionably established by techniques yet to be developed. We cannot postpone managing as effectively and honestly as possible the large number of children who present chronic differences we feel are more related to organicity variables than others."[7]

Ten characteristics of learning-disabled children most often cited by the contributors to this report, in order of frequency, are these:

1. Hyperactivity.
2. Perceptual-motor impairments.

---

[7] "Terminology and Identification," in *Minimal Brain Dysfunction in Children,* Washington, D.C.: U.S. Department of Health, Education, and Welfare, 1966, p. 7.

3. Emotional lability.
4. General coordination deficits.
5. Disorders of attention (short attention span, distractibility, perseveration).
6. Impulsivity.
7. Disorders of memory and thinking.
8. Specific learning disabilities:
   a. Reading.
   b. Arithmetic.
   c. Writing.
   d. Spelling.
9. Disorders of speech and hearing.
10. Equivocal neurological signs and electroencephalographic irregularities.

† † †

To catalog a series of symptoms is relatively easy. To take a youngster who is beginning life with a learning handicap and to hide him behind a label is both thoughtless and cruel. Goethe has said, "When knowledge is lacking, we give it a name." Many of the qualified people who work with children having learning disorders are distressed over the glib acceptance of labels. The term "learning disorder" does not talk of a clinical entity; it talks of children who have certain kinds of disabilities. Perhaps some of them were born with a unique kind of genetic makeup which affects the way they perceive and read; others have had emotional experiences or kinds of deprivation which have affected their own learning processes. Still others have suffered from injuries or illnesses which have left them crippled in some areas of their learning.

By the same token some of these children will progress remarkably with one type of therapy, others with another, and still others may need a combination of treatment. A child who cannot learn well through auditory stimuli may be able to remember words through the process of writing them on the blackboard, tracing them with his fingers, with his elbows, with his feet, until the words are indelibly etched into his mind. A youngster whose motor development is retarded may be aided through walking a plank, throwing a ball, exercising his muscles. The child with a hypersensitive auditory sense may thrive in an atmosphere where all is controlled and extremely quiet. Some children will improve with changed optical lenses and orthoptic training.

The shadow of cultism fades in the sunlight of a child's needs. Children cannot be placed statistically on charts or diagnosed neatly in reports. Because they are children, they have the needs of children and of all of us for success, for achievement, for a sense of order. They have disorders in various combinations and for various reasons. They must be seen singly and carefully. They must be observed, diagnosed, worked with on a painstaking and empathetic basis. It is a well known fact that a "simple" learning disorder can soon become overlaid with emotional problems if the child is not helped to conquer the difficulty.

In the eagerness to help with the problem, one is likely at times to forget the child himself and the meaningfulness of relationships to him. A story is told of a youngster with learning disabilities who was placed on a teaching machine in order that he could get continual reinforcement for his learning. He did well for several days, showing interesting improvement. Then came the days when he slipped back and made no further gains.

"Alvin," asked his regular teacher, "can you explain why you aren't improving your reading with that teaching machine? We had great hopes for it, and you."

Alvin worked a circle on the floor with his shoe toe, then looked up at his teacher and said, with perfect candor, "Aw, that teaching machine isn't fun any more. I can't get it to blow its fuse the way I could Miss Rose!"

It is certainly possible that the meaningfulness of relationships plays a giant part in any technique used for the teaching of children. It is easy to forget that the child himself is undergoing a series of disappointments and miseries and that he needs someone who can understand and help without being as baffled by his difficulties as he is himself.

What can happen to a child is that he is first surprised to discover that he cannot do what other children can; then he becomes frustrated; then angry. This anger might develop into sullenness and delinquency. The child obtains a negative self-image and guilt; then fear and a sense of hopelessness; then a compromise with his goals.

The great danger, according to the experts, is that one is likely to mistake the reaction to the problem for the cause of the problem. There must be careful and lengthy diagnostic work done to keep from confusing reaction with cause.

The confusion attendant to the many-sided approach to learning problems has been expressed in this way by Dr. C. E. Gorton of Texas Woman's University:

Each discipline or profession concerned with the problem of learning disabilities defines, develops theories, and treats the disability from his own frame of reference. The neurologist is concerned primarily with central nervous system pathology; the pediatrician with physiological pathology; the psychologist with behavioral abnormality; the educator with cognitive discrepancies; the sociologist with cultural norm deviations. As a result, individuals with learning disabilities are variously described as "educationally retarded," "autistic," "dyslexic," "perceptually handicapped," "minimally brain-injured," "emotionally disturbed," "neurologically disorganized," "dysgraphic," "aphasic," "interjacent," "word blind." Treatment procedures recommended range from psychotherapy, diet control, drug therapy, crawling, bead stringing, trampoline exercises, phonic drills, speech correction, tracing, orthoptic training, and auditory training drills.[8]

Yet Dr. Gorton goes on to state that the situation, instead of being hopeless, indicates that "the crux of the matter is not so much the validity of the descriptions and treatment procedures but rather for what sorts of individuals the descriptions and treatment are relevant."

It is always easier to focus on disability rather than on ability. In some instances the dysfunction can be an asset. For example, it has been discovered that people who are color blind are invaluable in seeing through camouflages. Now they are used in the armed forces to help spot enemy installations.

The child with learning problems also has many areas where he functions well. Yet if parents and educators ignore his competencies and concentrate totally on his lacks, he may soon give way to frustration and disappointment. Then he will acquire a self-image of failure and incompetence.

For example, if a youngster is highly verbal but cannot write, he might be encouraged to use a dictaphone or a tape recorder in making some of his reports. By so doing, he may acquire strength to work on the tedious process of practicing his writing skills. In this way the child will be having enough successes to help increase his tolerance for failure.

It is impossible to speak of learning disorders alone. What really concerns us are children—children with difficulties in learning. Some of the young people have problems for which they can compensate rather easily; others are so crippled by

[8] C. E. Gorton, "Professional Togetherness—an Unmet Need," in *Ideas for Action,* Vol. 2, No. 1, Houston, Texas: Texas Association for Children with Learning Disabilities, March 15, 1967, pp. 3–4.

their disabilities that they need specialized help over a period of months or years.

Even if the original problem is not highly damaging in itself, the overlay of emotional difficulties which come from successive failures may be a crippling factor. For example, a young child who is found to be deaf may, after a period of years, be fitted with a hearing aid. The mechanical aid is not enough unless help is also given to repair the damage which occurred to his personality and learning ability while he could not hear.

The child who suffers severely from learning disabilities is much like a satellite which continues to send out messages which no one receives. One young person who was having difficulties in school was asked to write a theme. Here is what he said: "I am a watermelon. I am lying on the sidewalk. I have a crack in my side, and all my pink is running out. I cry 'Help. Help.' Nobody comes."[9]

Whether the child's problems are indeterminate enough that all he feels is a continuous sense of failure or whether they are so gross that he becomes a school catastrophe, he lives with a sense of nonaccomplishment, a feeling of being different from other children, a knowledge of nagging failure. He cries "Help. Help." in his silent fashion. Who hears him?

[9] Arlene Barasch, "Tutoring Program Expands at the Y," from *"Y" Notes,* The University of Texas YMCA and YWCA, Austin, Texas, Fall 1965.

CHAPTER II

HOW THE DAMAGED CHILD VIEWS HIMSELF
"The Man Without a Mouth"

MANY PEOPLE MAY RECOGNIZE the silent cry for help without knowing what it signifies. A hyperactive, nonlearning child who precipitates series of crises and failures may demonstrate his fright but antagonize others while doing so. Like an animal trapped, he may snap at those who wish to free him.

Even the hypoactive child who is not a troublemaker shows his need for help through his failures and his subsequent withdrawal from people and from situations which call for skills he has not mastered.

If these children are baffling to those who would help them, they are even more puzzling to themselves. They are aware of their differences and often feel a sense of loss. The young people with serious learning disabilities are often like the mentally ill children because they have no competences to which to return. They may long vaguely for abilities they do not have, even though they do not hunger for some specific skill once known and forgotten.

We shall look at Sherry and Bruce, two children with serious learning disabilities, and we shall see how they seem to themselves. Then we shall discuss dyslexic, aphasic, and brain-damaged youngsters and learn what life is like for them.

The comfortable sameness by which most people moor their lives is unknown to the child with perceptual difficulties. For him the world is strange, ever-changing, always frightening. He is a tiny ship awash in a sea without compass, chart, or shipmate.

It is small wonder, then, that he reacts to this ever-changing scene with anxiety, with fright, with hyperactivity, or with unwillingness to leave any haven. Without rhythm, without regularity, without a spirit of tranquility, he remains suspicious and fearful of the next move.

And the worst of it is that he cannot express his fright, for it has always been a part of his being. He has nothing with which to compare it; no shore where he has been moored; no cove where he has lain secure and warm.

For the child with serious learning problems, every scene —perched, fragmented, or twirling—is unlike any other. And each child is endeavoring with all of his abilities to adjust to the world he perceives. He cannot see the universe through the eyes of society or of his parents but has to respond to it as it appears to him.

For most of us life is a sequence of expected happenings —sunrise and sunset, tides entering and leaving the shoreline, first star and new moon followed by expanding and shrinking moons. Day after day we know the pattern of a heartbeat, the shape of a familiar room, the design of our dishes.

Life, with all of its unexpected happenings, is underlaced with regularity, with assurance of enough sameness to hold one steady in a changing world. The morning news may bring startling facts, but it is heard and seen on the familiar television set. The drive to work may be frightening because of a near-accident, but the steering wheel and seats and windshield are the same as the ones the day before.

Without the stability of the "constants" on which one can count, one would find the world not only new but often fearsome with every waking moment. The moving planes of wallpaper, ceiling, and floor would keep one tilted and uncertain. The various perceptions of oneself in a glass would resemble the look into a carnival house of mirrors.

The story is told of a little boy who entered a hospital for the first time. A mechanical speaker from the nurses' station was in the wall right above his head. After his parents had left him, the small boy huddled under the covers, alone in the room. The head nurse spoke from her station, saying, "Johnny, are you all right?" There was no answer. She asked again, louder. Still no answer. Finally the nurse said, "All right, Johnny, I know you are in there. Answer me." The boy rolled his eyes upward and said, "What do you want, wall?"

Just so the child with learning disabilities is unable to obtain meaningful information about the world and his place in it. For him, the wall may speak and give commands.

He may respond in inappropriate ways to stimuli. And his response, to those who cannot understand the base for his behavior, is bizarre. It is much like the reaction of a person who was eyewitness to a prolonged gun battle and who, for many months, jumped with extreme fright at the bursting of a balloon. So does the child with learning disabilities react in varied ways to stimuli.

Life for the child with serious perceptual handicaps is filled with scenes which shift and turn and offer no "anchor" to hold him steady. He often cannot separate what is relevant from what is irrelevant. In the schoolroom he may begin by looking at a problem the teacher has put on the board and be distracted by the gold pin on her dress or the buckle of her belt or the pattern of sunlight on the floor. Some professionals have thought that, instead of talking of the child's lack of attention, discussion ought to center on the fact that the child pays too much attention to everything. He is unable to "sort out," "stack up," "sift" experiences in a fashion which helps him organize his hour or his day or his life.

How can a youngster share a dream with one who has not had the same kind of dream as he? Can he describe a need when he does not have the symbols or the tools to explain it?

Can he convey the pain of aloneness, the joy of human contact, or the ache of longing without a common base of known experience? He cannot.

Rather, the child with severe learning problems stands on shifting sands. No foundation holds him steady, firm, upright. Each awakening is a new struggle to learn where the boundaries of life extend, to know which is sky and which is land.

The fright and the uncertainty can be attested to by Sherry and by Bruce, two young people who had serious perceptual problems, who knew that something was wrong with them, and yet who could not convey to others the measure of their misery or their disability.

Take Sherry first. Any little girl with a tumble of golden curls and a dimple should find the world a cream puff to be opened easily and softly tasted. But for Sherry the world is more in the nature of an ocean. Each high wave hides the shoreline, pitches her at an angle, obscures what is familiar. And Sherry spends her days battling against the uncertainty of a world which will not stay still.

Her pink bookcase is filled with picture books, big ones, cloth ones, and small editions. Sherry opens one and sees a large gray poodle staring at her. Daddy comes in, takes her on his lap, cuddles her head against his chest, then points to the picture and says, "Doggie." Sherry obediently responds. And the two of them are content together until Daddy finds another picture, this time a terrier running after a boy. "What is that, Sherry?" Daddy asks softly. But Sherry does not know. She does not know, and she does not understand why Daddy grows impatient and sometimes angry, why he tries again and again with pictures which are always different and ever-changing. Sherry cannot relate one picture to another or one object with its counterpart. There is, for her, no "form constancy."

Now Sherry goes to school. And here the confusion deepens, widens, and troubles her constantly. She has painfully tried to recognize the same object in different forms and shapes and positions. And now she sits at her small desk in the classroom. She holds her hands tightly because the fear she has felt so often before begins to engulf her. It is like a cloud which settles over her body and clouds her vision of everyone. The teacher puts the alphabet on the board. The little girl next to Sherry, Jane with the square bangs, giggles and begins to copy the letters on her tablet. But for Sherry the jungle is real. Now a letter which is called a "b" can be rotated and become something entirely different, a "d." Or, with a tail, it is a "q," or turned around, a "g." Sherry begins to shake with the fright of a three-foot girl faced with an eight-foot problem. She cannot see over, around, or beyond the giant which is her disability.

Sherry covers her paper to keep competent Jane from seeing her. She is both confused and scared, and pretty soon she stops trying to copy those strange figures from the blackboard. Miss Angus walks around the room, nods at Jane, but stops to frown over Sherry's paper. Her voice becomes acid-tinged as she says, "Sherry, you're not trying. Copy from the board."

What Miss Angus does not know is that Sherry *is* trying, with all of the ability and competence she can muster. What Sherry does not know is that soon her lack of adequacy with form constancy may be multiplied by her lack of ability to put together usefully what she sees and hears.

Sherry's dimple does not show very often any more. She is a little girl in trouble, and inside of her, she knows it. She knows it but does not comprehend what to say to Mother or to Daddy, who are so eager that she do well in school, that she learn to read, that she know success and more success after that.

Sherry walks alone out of her classroom. The corridor is very long.

No one really recognizes yet that Sherry is in trouble. But Bruce has many difficulties, and lots of people know that there are problems. Not very many have an idea of what they really are.

For Bruce it has been a game of hide-and-seek since he was a little boy. Hiding the kind of problem he has kept having and seeking some way to get around it or over it. Bruce is stupid. Of that he is sure, and every morning when he wakes, he lies in bed for minutes wondering how he can get out of going to school. Bruce lies there looking at his baseball mitt and wishing that he could run out of the house and catch some balls, get into a good, solid, long-running game of baseball and forget school and all that it implies.

But alarm clock, Mother's voice, Dad's admonition, sister Kathy's tittering, all intrude, and Bruce tries to swallow the lump of fear which lies in his breast whenever it is time for school. When you're ten years old and have been going to school for four years, that is a lot of lumps! If he has to repeat the fourth grade, Kathy is going to catch up with him and go by. And that Bruce cannot endure. He wishes he were old enough to hop a train or work on a farm or join up with a ball club—anything but face school and another day of reading, reading, writing, and more writing. Math isn't too bad. He can pitch in and make sense of that, but reading bugs him. He must be stupid. If he wasn't, he could read. Everyone knows that, and lots of people tell him so.

Bruce thinks of the day ahead—the hours at school, with Miss Rankin calling him down for not turning in his theme, for not reading his lesson. And there might be a fight on the playground. There sure will be if Ralph starts teasing him again or calls him stupid one more time. Only today he will rub Ralph's eyes and nose in the playground dirt instead of just roughing him up a little. That's how he feels. And he means it. In fact, he wishes he could line up five or six of the fellows—and Miss Rankin too—and hit them all. Stupid. Stupid. Stupid!

As Bruce dresses, he remembers the fun he had at camp last summer. Gosh, he'd like to go back, but Mother and Dad said he wouldn't be allowed to do so unless he brings his grades way up. In fact, Mother said she would work with him all summer on his reading, just like she's been doing every night. Every night Bruce sits in the den with Mother and hears the tantalizing calls of the kids down the street. He listens for the crack of ball on bat and wishes himself away from the book he holds and into the vacant lot two houses away.

"Try, Bruce, try." How many times has he heard that statement? A million? Maybe two million. What can a guy do? Can a ten-year-old fellow tell his father that he has terrible dreams every night? And that he is plain scared to go to school? It would be pretty hard to explain to Dad, especially since Dad is already reading him the riot act for getting into so many fights. A fellow can't squeal on the other guys either and tell Dad that they tease him, all the time, every day, day after day. A guy can only stand so much without taking a swing.

Kathy, with her tittering and her girl friends, bugs him too. Sure he is grumpy to her. In fact, the whole family makes him tired. And that is why he spends so much time in his room.

So there is Bruce. Ten years old. Fighting mad, and with good reason. And there are his bewildered parents and his well-meaning teacher. They cannot see inside of him the frightened, nonachieving youngster who would like, better than anything, to be able to read effortlessly and to write themes his teacher would praise.

The inability to read may seem like one point on a continuum to some people. To Bruce and to the children like him it is a dye which colors all of life and which poisons everything they touch. Bruce sees himself only as a stupid boy who has little worth. For him the disability is real, profound, and hurtful.

For Sherry and Bruce it does not matter greatly what label is put upon their disability. They know that they are unlike other people, that they fail where their peers succeed, that they cannot achieve what others can. Even for the child whose learning problems are not severe enough to remove him from school, there is the constant corrosion of failure blighting the "finish" of a personality and making dark and rough what should shine.

† † †

Categories serve to narrow what they name. There is no "pure" dyslexia or aphasia or brain-damage. Instead the difficulties overlap. Children generally have a combination of problems, and the following definitive statements of problem areas are used only to help shape the discussion. Often the classification lists only the major problem or the most disabling one.

Dyslexia

"Dyslexia" is only a name or a label. The child with problems is real and needy. Let us look at five dyslexic children and see how they differ from one another and yet how similar they are in their reactions to the strange world which is their home.

Butch, David, Marcy, Frank, and Nicky can describe dyslexia in their own behavior.

A boy comparable to Bruce was a chubby little guy named Butch. That was not his real name, of course. He was christened Jonathan Edmund, but he has been Butch from the beginning. Although he is only partially dyslexic—one of the lucky ones—his pattern of continual failure and near-failure finally sent his parents for professional help. And by the time they received such aid, Butch was already scarred with the burns of failure.

Let's go back and see what life was like for Butch. He was a pleasant baby. His broad shoulders gave him the look of a miniature football player. With two older sisters, he became the gratifying male figure to his father, and little of a scholastic nature was required of him in his first five years.

Because he was only partially dyslexic, Butch's speech and vocabulary were average, his articulation unimpaired, his comprehension of orally presented verbal situations superior, and his insight into the relationships of word-concepts above normal.

It was when school and Butch met that trouble flared, a smoldering problem became a flame. Butch gave no indication of being part of the family which contained two achieving young women, who added further insult to Butch's injury by reciting in school programs.

While his sisters were moving with the top level of students and bringing home report cards replete with A's, Butch found himself in an environment which seemed hostile, strange, and threatening. For some reason the "computer" in his brain could not process the symbolic data given to him with the accuracy and speed expected of his age group. Learning to perceive, symbolize, comprehend, and reproduce symbols became all-important, and Butch's athletic prowess and genial nature faded into the shadows.

Butch hobbled along with the barest of achievement patterns until he was ten years old. He went from one grade to another carrying his handicap as an old man would shoulder a bundle up a hill. He was "blessed" by having a problem of only moderate difficulty. Therefore, he was not far enough behind his class to come to dramatic notice of the teachers; yet, as his medical summary stated, "Each year the patient encountered more and more difficult scholastic work."

Although Butch could read fairly well, his main problems were with multisyllable words, demonstrating that he would get further and further behind as classwork became increasingly difficult. Because reading was such an unsatisfying chore, he soon lost interest in the printed page and would not complete assignments unless someone sat beside him to help him finish. In spelling, he was several years behind his peer groups, and in arithmetic he could barely keep up with the class.

When a psychologist began to test Butch, he found the youngster agreeable, cooperative, and more than a little angry that he should fail so completely where his peers succeeded. To the parents the psychologist explained that intelligence cannot always be seen by IQ scores but is dependent upon qualities which may be measurable in some ways but which are not assessed by the IQ test. IQ's, according to the psychologist, cannot be gauged independently of personality factors. They do not outline the level of integration or reveal the personality and emotional structure upon which the intellect is superimposed.

Butch revealed superior quantitative ratings by the psychologist's standards, but he could not master the basic fundamentals of reading and writing. Because he was so bright, because he could compensate in some measure for his handicap, Butch was thought to be lazy or lacking in motivation. Until the testing, no one could know how much effort it took for Butch to master the reading assignments or prepare his homework.

The same factors held true for Butch's writing assignments. Since fine-muscle coordination was uncertain, he had trouble with his written work and often did not complete it.

In tests of verbal functions other than language *per se,* Butch tested out at age ranges from ten years and six months to almost sixteen years—and this when he was ten years old and almost failing in some of his school subjects! In tests requiring him to use precise and fine-muscle coordination, he tested at slightly over seven years.

Because he had known so few successes, because trying had brought so few rewards, Butch was poorly disciplined in mental processes. He was dependent on his family and commanded attention through his dependency. He wanted to be the focus of attention in all his relationships.

Thus, Butch had a twofold job to accomplish when his trouble was finally diagnosed. He needed to be helped through special tutorial programs in the areas of dyslexia. Also, he had to be helped to grow in maturity and to overcome the immature patterns he had developed during his troubled years in school.

DAVID

David, a remarkable man who reached his late twenties without being able to read or write, can speak for the person with learning disabilities. Life for him was a series of abrasive school failures and continual life failures until one day, in his early twenties, he turned on educational television and found that he could learn by watching and listening. He selected children's encyclopedias and laboriously made out some of the pages. He bought recommended books and gave them to his friends to read, quizzing them about the contents. He painted and composed music, dictating lyrics to a friend who knew of his incapacity.

As he learned, he became aware of what he was missing, of what life could offer and of what he could contribute. He hungered.

What is it like not to be able to read or write? Let him tell you through a letter he dictated to his doctor:

I took a deep look at man that night, and I saw man as a material extension of the will that fills a vacuum that brings things together and makes something else. With this revived awareness, my hunger was that of a vacuum, and I seek to fill the vacuum and feel the hunger of man's world. But what of mistakes and the speed of time? And I thought, man's successes and failures of past and present are frozen in twisted symbols on millions and millions of pages for anyone who can melt the symbols into thought.

And my ears heard my mouth speak these words: I can not! I have not! I never will! And my anger and emotions grew with the echo of each word in my mind. And in a fit of anger, I hurled a black book across the room, crying "No," to the echo and then in a soft voice, I said, "I will learn if it kills me."

A year later, this man was able to dictate the following sentences in a letter to artists whom he had met on a vacation.

I feel like a fast growing tree in a damp sunny forest, always finding myself at sunrise taller and stronger.

The complexity of the reading process is recognized by all authorities. Dr. Frostig explains why the teaching of reading cannot be accomplished in a set of easy lessons. She says,

Reading . . . is a complicated process. Many skills are involved in gleaning meaning from the printed page. The words
have to be recognized, their forms associated with sound
patterns, and the sound patterns in turn associated with meaning. This chain of associations depends on correct visual and
auditory perception, language, memory, and thought. If there
is one weak link in the chain of associations, the process
of reading will be distorted or interrupted. It is important for
the teacher to realize that optimum remediation depends on
careful diagnostic exploration, because remediation has to
vary according to the disturbance. No single teaching method
can be the correct approach for all children.[1]

MARCY

Marcy was almost thirteen before her difficulties became so apparent to everyone that she was referred by the visiting teacher
in her school for diagnostic testing. As the psychiatrist who
studied her said, "In psychiatric interview it was evident that
this girl seemed to have lost confidence in her ability to learn
to read." In other areas Marcy was delightful. Again, the psychiatrist noted, "She was a pleasant, warm, rather passive girl,
who related well to the interview. She seemed to have varied
interests in that her hobbies are painting, singing, and danc-
ing."

However, the hobbies were not enough to compensate for
the disabilities. Marcy's once-even temper was beginning to
flare with little provocation. She was often angry and bellig-
erent toward her younger sister who had no reading problem.
Marcy's friends came to the house at less frequent intervals
after being pelted with blasts of Marcy's temper. And the
circular pattern of isolation was beginning to close around

[1] Marianne Frostig, "The Needs of Teachers for Specialized Information on Reading," in *The Teacher of Brain-Injured Children,* William M.
Cruickshank, ed., New York: Syracuse University Press, 1966, p. 90.

Marcy. Despite the fact that Marcy had a loving family and concerned parents, she was starting to show signs of withdrawal and despair.

Marcy was a tiny island surrounded by a frightening sea. For example, examination showed that "she had gross orientational defects in time and space. She did not know the seasons, the date, nor the month. She did not know when Easter, her favorite holiday, was and she could not tell how far her home was from downtown nor how long it took to get there."

If a girl like Marcy, whose problems had not been gross enough to attract professional attention until she was twelve, suffered so many kinds of "displacements" in space and time, the plight of the child with severe disabilities must be magnified a hundred times. Such a child is an astronaut with no ground crew to guide him, a person floating in space without knowledge of the forces which could hold him steady.

FRANK

Take Frank. He, too, was twelve years old when his scholastic problems brought him to psychiatric attention. In fact, his difficulties at school were so large that the question was raised concerning possible mental retardation.

Frank's actions in the classroom were disruptive and disturbing, although his mother noted that his behavior at home was without problem. If he had not had school difficulties, he would never have come to the attention of a clinic.

When Frank was tested in the language clinic, he showed severe retardation in all aspects of reading, his scores in general falling approximately six years below that expected for his mental age. His overall reading level was at a high second grade, and the language instructor noted that Frank made many substitutions, that his reading rate was extremely slow, and that he struggled very hard with the work, doing much subvocal pronunciation as he attempted silent reading. Interestingly enough, Frank's arithmetic competence was a great deal higher than his reading, and he was able to do above seventh grade work in math.

But, like Marcy, Frank was marked with the ink of failure, and the marking colored other aspects of his life. The psychiatrist noted that Frank had much anxiety, much reactive guilt to his school failure, impaired motivation, and other feelings which were expressed in his acting-out behavior.

For Frank the recommendation was for special help via reading and psychotherapy. Because Frank's reading problem had dragged through the sand of many years of failure, it was felt that his reading would improve very little, even with intensive care.

NICKY

There is much more hope for Nicky. Blond-haired Nicky has an appealing smile, but his blue eyes seem a bit frightened and bewildered. No wonder. Nicky is not yet seven, but he has had double failure. Already he has been in the second grade twice and has been unable to achieve competence to move ahead. His peers—Helen and Mike and Jimmy and Fred—have all gone on to the third grade, leaving Nicky behind. The aura of defeat lies across his freckled face.

When he was tested, Nicky approached each new task with great fear of failure. He had trouble expressing himself verbally, and he carried himself with the air of a child who knows he will not succeed.

Complicating Nicky's problem is his parents' lack of insight. They pressure him constantly to read, to read better, to read more, failing to recognize that Nicky does not read because he cannot. In his testing, he showed himself to be "totally illiterate and functioning at a poor preprimer level."

The question always arises in young children concerning whether the lack of reading skills comes from severe reading retardation or from "developmental lag," which will lessen as the child grows older. In the instance of Nicky, the recommendations took both matters into consideration. The report stated, "It probably would be wise now to handle the situation on the basis of the latter etiologic formulation which would mean special education for Nicky now. He is clearly aware of and sensitive to his disability and is becoming more and more withdrawn. Emotional blocking is now complicating the primary problem and this will make learning increasingly difficult in the months ahead. For this reason it would be best to offer Nicky remedial work now."

WHAT THE EXPERTS SAY

Dyslexia, as we have seen, may be minor or severe. Most of the children suffering from specific dyslexia are normal or above in intelligence but are youngsters whose perceptual and cognitive disabilities have kept them from learning to read by conventional methods.

What looks like simple dyslexia, however, may often be symptomatic of a deep and underlying difficulty. An example might be a boy who was referred to a specialized program for help with his reading. He was diagnosed as dyslexic. The physician knew the family and realized that the boy was undergoing some severe emotional problems because of an absent father and a mother who was very ill. The problems with reading merely signified the problems he was having in many other areas of his life.

Troubles frequently start to creep into the dyslexic child's life when he begins to go to school. Suddenly, like Sherry, he is confronted with a world in which circles and curves of chalk on board must take meaning, where pencil on paper must form symbols understood by others, where black marks in books give facts. And then he begins to worry in earnest. Because the dyslexic child often sees words in reverse: "saw" becomes "was"; "not" becomes "ton." He may not be able to see "girl" or "boy" but may find them as "gril" or "yob." In addition, as Sherry discovered, letters that can be reversed, moved up or down, undo him. For a child who cannot see the letters as they are, reading becomes a cruel task which tries his skill and his patience and which leaves him feeling inadequate, frustrated, angry, and rebellious.

Such reversals are part of the characteristics of very young children and are not significant unless the deviations are severe. It is only when a child continues to have real problems with such reversals and with reading after he is seven, that careful study should be made of the child and his abilities.

Dyslexic children and adults too have some particular difficulty in learning the conventional meaning of verbal symbols and of associating the sound with the symbol in appropriate fashion. Sometimes they cannot pronounce an unfamiliar word; or they cannot hear the differences between words; they cannot detect ear differences in the sounds of words or letters; they have difficulty in switching from right to left hand, or difficulty in reading with sufficient understanding. For example, some of the children may be taught which is their right and which is their left hand. Yet they may get all mixed up when told, "Write your name in the upper right-hand corner of the paper." They have been able to learn through reinforcement about right and left, but they cannot translate that learning into action.

At one clinic for dyslexic people the story is told of a young man who had made it through high school because of constant tutoring by his mother. However, he could not read or compute figures adequately. His great love was cars, and he was a superb mechanic. Perhaps he would never have come for help had he not made a serious error in billing. He made out a bill for $18 instead of $81 and was too ashamed to ask his customer for the additional money. Then he recognized that he would need help in his ability to read and write.

In every city there are professional persons—physicians, teachers, businessmen, and volunteer workers—who have grown up and gone through college despite the fact that they are slightly dyslexic and still have troubles with reversals in their reading.

One well-known clinic for language disorders has a file of papers by a young scientist, a brilliant man. He cannot write a sentence which anyone can read. Not only is his writing bad, but he has no spelling whatsoever. However, his abilities are so great that he is able to use Dictaphones and telephones and telegrams to convey his ideas and is able to bypass writing altogether.

Katrina de Hirsch, head of the Pediatric Language Disorder Clinic at the Presbyterian Medical Center in New York, says, "Children with reading disabilities are not as totally disabled emotionally as are youngsters who lack words for expression and communication. Nevertheless, reading failure frequently results in an impaired self-image, and many children become social and emotional casualties as a result of early defeat."[2]

She explains that some children use all of their psychic energy in trying to get their bearings. Her long-time work with preschool children who subsequently developed reading, spelling, and writing difficulties has demonstrated to her that these often very intelligent youngsters show marked lags in a num-

[2] Katrina de Hirsch, Jeannette Jefferson Jansky, and William S. Langford, *Predicting Reading Failure,* New York: Harper and Row, 1966, p. xiv (Ref. no. 97).

ber of areas: their fine-motor skills are often inadequate, they are slow in inserting pegs into a board, and they are clumsy in handling a pencil. Their human figure drawings are primitive. Their ability to copy geometric forms is inferior. They show gaps in both understanding and use of oral language. It is difficult for them to discriminate between words which sound alike; they sometimes fail to understand the gist of a story. They use rudimentary sentence construction and have trouble with naming. Their ability to tell a story from pictures or from memory is limited. They do relatively poorly on tests requiring them to match similar-looking words or combinations exposed in the correct and reversed order. In short, in spite of good intellectual endowment, they show marked immaturity in many aspects of functioning.

Mrs. de Hirsch estimates that about three to seven per cent of the population suffers from dyslexia, that is to say, from severe reading, writing, and spelling disabilities. For some reason, boys outnumber girls in this disorder by almost three to one, and there seems to be some genetic component to the problem.

Actual figures on the numbers of youngsters who get into real trouble because of their reading inaccuracies are difficult to obtain. An estimate frequently heard is that about ten per cent of all children of intelligence normal or above have reading problems. If, as is thought, about two-thirds of them have moderate to very severe difficulties, that means that there are about two million to three million children in the United States at present with reading problems. Not all of them, of course, are dyslexic or brain-damaged.

These youngsters begin signaling when they are four, five, or six that they are beginning to have trouble with perceptual-motor functions. As has been seen, when they are in grades one, two, and three, the troubles are very apparent both to themselves and to the teachers.

The spillover problems are enormous. According to Dr. John Money:

> Severe specific dyslexia and generalized mental deficiency both delay the acquisition of literacy. But they do more. They permanently limit the level of literacy finally attained. In the case of specific dyslexia, the degree of final impairment of literacy appears to be inversely related to the IQ and to the caliber of mental abilities not dyslexically affected.[3]

The neurological view of developmental dyslexia has been stated thus by Dr. Macdonald Critchley:

> There exists, within the community of poor readers, a specific syndrome wherein particular difficulty exists in learning the conventional meaning of symbols. Such cases are earmarked, it has been said, by their gravity and by their purity. This syndrome is of constitutional and not of environmental origin, and is often genetically determined.

In his paper Dr. Critchley also points out that disorders of writing quite frequently accompany those of reading, including

> . . . an overall untidiness of penmanship, malalignment; intrusion of block capitals into the middle of a word; omissions or repetitions of words; rotation of letters; odd punctuation marks; and misspellings. . . . Still less familiar, but highly typical, is the dyslexic's failure to spell in numbers.[4]

[3] John Money, "Progress and Research Needs in Dyslexia," in *Reading Disability,* Baltimore: Johns Hopkins Press, 1961, p. 10.

[4] Macdonald Critchley, "Inborn Reading Disorders of Central Origin," from *Transactions of the Ophthalmological Society,* Vol. LXXXL, 1961, p. 465.

In speaking of disorders in spatial manipulation, Dr. Critchley points out that many dyslexic children have an inadequate sense of rhythm. Many of the younger ones have poor muscular coordination and may not find it easy to bounce or throw a ball or to fasten buttons on their clothes.

The emotional unhappiness which may accompany dyslexia is noted by Dr. Critchley also. He says,

> One of the most telling arguments for early diagnosis, segregation and special treatment, is the ease with which dyslexic children develop neurotic reactions to their disability. . . . The dyslexic is an alien in a critical if not hostile milieu, mocked, misunderstood, or penalized; cut off from opportunities for advancement. As an adult he is devoid of cultural advantages; he is doomed to a second class citizenship; blind to the printed instructions, appeals, exhortations, and information with which he is surrounded.[5]

He continues to say that the tendency too often prevails to look upon the problem as an environmental or psychogenic one, giving the child little incentive to persevere in his arduous task of learning to read.

Dr. Critchley recognizes that to identify the cases of specific developmental dyslexia among the multitude of poor readers is difficult. A wide range of skills and much knowledge are demanded of the diagnostician, who must also have an open mind concerning treatment and methods of helping the child. Because of the diversity of symptoms and their manifestation, diagnosis requires many tests and much knowledge of the patient's background, family, and environment.

All of the experts agree that reading disability is not ever a single entity or the only one troubling the child. Combinations of problems have been evident in some way in all of the children who have been described.

[5] *Ibid.,* p. 466.

OTHER DISTURBANCES

One disturbance is in orientation. We have noted that some of the children have problems in learning where they are, which is right and which is left, which is north and which south. This kind of disturbance keeps a child at a loss in many of his daily activities. One doctor told of asking a young boy which of two doctors was taller. It happened that one was 6'5" and the other little more than 5'5". The youngster was thoroughly confused about which one was indeed taller. When asked what height he thought the taller doctor might be, he said, "Five feet."

Another difficulty shown by many of these children is an inability to read maps and blueprints. This problem means that the child cannot "symbolize" in spatial areas. In a classroom situation calling for such abilities, as, for example, the study of geography, he is lost.

The inability to learn the significance of sequence and time has been evidenced by several of the children described. This difficulty was dramatized by Marcy, who did not know how far her home was from downtown nor how long it took to get from one place to the other.

Trouble with writing is a frequent disturbance of such children, as are serious spelling problems. Because spelling in written form demands the ability to see and hear letters simultaneously, it poses a real problem for children with learning disabilities.

In Frank's case, his arithmetic skills were much better than his reading. However, a deficiency in being able to understand the symbolic significance of numbers is frequent among nonlearners. Sometimes the young people cannot read numbers or cannot associate the meaning with the arithmetical symbols.

Difficulty with foreign language frequently occurs in children who have serious disabilities in learning. Johnny, who had had encephalitis, was able to make up most of his scholastic deficiencies, with the exception of foreign language. When he went to college, he had to find a major which would be acceptable without such requirements. As Johnny said, "My therapist told me that I had had a hard enough time learning the English language. It would be cruel to try to learn another."

Various kinds of memory disorders are suffered by children with brain dysfunction. Some of the children have great problems with trying to remember sequences of numbers. Some, like Polly, cannot remember what they have read or learned. Others cannot recall sets of instructions. The teacher who asks her pupils to "open your books; get out your colors; put your notebooks in the upper right-hand corner of your desk" may lose the child in the first few words.

The above listing of various kinds of disabilities merely demonstrates the variety of combinations of disorders which may present themselves to the child with dyslexia. No one child—fortunately—has all of the disabilities nor any special combination.

Thus, it is easy to recognize why the authorities state that there is no such entity as a simple reading disorder. All such disorders seem to be part of other weaknesses or lacks of capacity in certain areas.

Childhood Aphasia

A childhood disorder, relatively new to the literature, is that of childhood aphasia. A brief look at this disability may show again how complex and "unneat" it is and how hard to categorize in a box labeled "brain damage" or some other title.

Aphasia in adults has long been recognized. The person having a stroke often loses his abilities to speak or even to recognize the spoken or written word. But aphasia in children was often confused with mental retardation, deafness, or a psychosis of some kind.

Aphasia is defined as being the loss or impairment of the power to use or understand speech, resulting from brain lesion, or, sometimes, from functional or emotional disturbance.[6]

"Language is one of the most potent forces in social life; it welds together smaller or greater communities and makes them something more than a number of isolated individuals."[7] Let us look at these isolated individuals.

FRED

At the age of four Fred is newborn every morning to a world in which he cannot express his needs or understand the words of anyone else. Nothing is labeled, anchored, fixed. He opens his eyes, sees the familiar room, recognizes its familiarity without being able to pinpoint the names of items. He knows that he exists—but it is on an island surrounded by strange and noisy waters.

His mother comes into the room. She smiles at Fred, a smile he feels as a ship feels anchor. She leans over Fred, rumples his hair. He knows the warm and searching fingers, sees the loving look. She opens her mouth and makes sounds which Fred cannot fathom. She speaks louder, but only the garbled noise comes through. Somehow Fred knows that a response is expected, but he does not know what. Finally she gestures to Fred to get out of bed. The warm fingers, the smiles have disappeared. As Fred stands on the floor, feels the discomfort

[6] *Webster's New International Dictionary,* Second edition, Springfield, Massachusetts: G. & C. Merriam Company, 1959.
[7] *Encyclopaedia Britannica,* Vol. 13, p. 697.

of the cold, he is aware that he is isolated from the people in his family who are able to make noises to one another and to sit close together as they do so.

Sometimes when Mother gets impatient and makes certain sounds like, "Do you want to eat?" Fred is able to hear and to say to Mother, "Do you want to eat?" But she does not smile. And Fred does not smile much any more either. He contents himself with rolling toys with which he can play alone.

If life is confusing to the normal child who is trying to sort out his family structure, his own place in the world, his belongings, and his surroundings, for the aphasic child the task is monumental. All of these children have trouble in the primary necessity, that of communication.

The two kinds of aphasia which may be manifest are expressive aphasia or apraxia and receptive aphasia or agnosia, or these may be mixed. In expressive aphasia the child lacks adequate responsive language; he may be able to say one or two syllables at a time. He has good understanding of speech, but cannot orally and/or graphically communicate his idea to others. In other words, he can understand what is said to him, but he may not be able to repeat or respond symbolically to such sounds. As a young child, he makes his wishes known by grunting, pointing, or pulling someone toward the object he desires.

Everyone who has had some difficulty in communicating, at any level, can picture what it must be like to be aphasic. A very minute example of expressive aphasia can be given by persons who cannot sing. Many of them hear tunes which play in their heads. They can "think" the tunes, can "hear" them, can certainly recognize them when they are played, but they are totally unable to hum or sing them in recognizable fashion to someone else.

If the aphasia is receptive, the child lacks understanding

of speech or writing. He may also lack expressive speech and show a great discrepancy between his intelligence and his understanding of the spoken language and between his hearing and understanding of spoken language. He may be totally silent, or may have scribble speech, or may imitate speech. He may be likened to the person who listens to a foreign diplomat speaking on television. The listener may be aware of the feeling tone and the sounds of words without being able to understand any of the content.

CAROLYN

Pretty Carolyn, petite, appealing. Object for admiration from all of the relatives. The kind of girl whom people stop to admire or to gurgle over. But Carolyn is aphasic, a problem which may not show itself during the first year of life.

It is when sister Lois is born that troubles really begin. Although Lois is not as pretty as Carolyn, she begins to give satisfaction to her parents and other family members immediately. She calls "Mama" and "Daddy" and is able to cuddle with them and say, "You sweet" and "I love you."

Carolyn soon senses that the most important people in her life, her parents, are turning to Lois for joys and special delights. More and more she watches, an involuntary spectator at her own life drama. Without being able to verbalize what is wrong, she still recognizes that it is she who is different, out of step, and isolated.

Because she longs for attention and needs to be noticed, Carolyn lashes out at Lois. And when she does, her mother and father move in swiftly to punish her. Carolyn's despair turns to anger and her anger to despair. She alternates between staying in her room, mute and alone, or acting out through temper tantrums her complete sense of frustration.

For Carolyn life is a series of disappointments. She wakes

to a world of noise without meaning. She cannot respond to her sister, her mother, or her father in many ways which give them pleasure. She is "a stranger in a strange land" where she neither understands nor speaks the language.

Carolyn is aphasic; does she know what life could be if she had the usual competencies for speech and hearing?

Carolyn knows that her world is different from that occupied by her mother and father and sister. She lives in a place of sound without meaning. She feels herself inside a plastic bubble where she can see and know about those she loves without ever being able to reach them in a meaningful fashion.

Do these children know that they are different?

BERNARD

Bernard can give the answer. Let one young psychologist tell about Bernard.

> He was a little guy, six years old, scrub team size. His hair was red and bushy, and there were more freckles than skin tone visible. He looked like a kid who could take care of himself in a fight, and judging from some of the scars on his legs, he had had the opportunity to prove it.
>
> Anyone seeing him for the first time would have thought that this young man would be able to get through school with no problems. He was obviously bright. One could tell that in the blue eyes which seemed to penetrate as they stared at you. And if you were observant, you could see that the eyes were troubled, windows to an uneasy spirit.
>
> I knew, of course, that the kid had no speech, although he did say a few syllables which were understandable from time to time. I let him know that our hour together would be mostly fun and that I wanted to be a friend of his. Then we began with the "Draw a Man" test. Bernard picked up his pencil and

cradled his arm around the paper. He drew laboriously. Finally, when he handed me the paper, I had a hard time keeping my feelings to myself.

For Bernard had drawn a man without a mouth![8]

The man without a mouth. Bernard was able to convey with his pencil and his paper the damage which he recognized in himself. He let the psychologist know that he too recognized that he was not whole.

† † †

What are some of the ways in which Bernard and Carolyn and Fred can develop the powers of speech and the competencies of communication? What is the future for an aphasic child? Who helps him? And how?

As always, diagnosis becomes the vital first step. To be certain that the child is aphasic and not psychotic or autistic becomes important. The task is difficult but necessary.

Because none of the disturbances discussed here stands still in their fixed categories, the problem of identification and aid enlarges. For example, many nonlanguage children have many kinds of handicaps. Some suffer primarily from emotional disturbances, with the aphasia as a secondary manifestation. For the former, educational methods for the deaf will be ineffective. For the latter, techniques for teaching aphasic children will be of little use until the emotional problem is alleviated.

The differential diagnosis becomes the vital step toward helping the child with problems. Although all children with learning difficulties share many hardships together, it must also

[8] Lillian F. Wilson, "Characteristics of Aphasia in Children," in *Childhood Aphasia and Brain Damage: A Definition,* Sheldon R. Rappaport, ed., Narberth, Pennsylvania: Livingston Publishing Company, 1963, p. 16.

be recognized that there are differences with all of the implications which those differences imply.

This explanation might help to differentiate the two problems:

> For teaching purposes, the aphasic child is one who shows characteristic deficiencies in the acquisition of speech and language that exceed those predictable on the basis of his demonstrated intelligence, hearing, and emotional status. In turn, the hyperkinetic brain-damaged child is one who has suffered some type of brain insult that . . . manifests itself in a syndrome of response patterns reflecting the ego dysfunctions of inadequate impulse control or regulation, inadequate integrative functions, and defective self-concept with attendant narcissistic hypersensitivity.[9]

The report goes on to say that both groups need some very highly specialized educational programs which can meet the specific needs they demonstrate. The differences between the two are that the aphasic children generally have little behavioral disturbances because of their aphasia, especially if the problem is diagnosed early enough that the children have not built up mountainous peaks of emotional problems to accompany those they already have in speech and language. For the hyperkinetic brain-damaged child, on the other hand, psychotherapy is nearly always needed to help him overcome the deficits which have damaged the development of his ego. It is further added that both parents and teachers should understand the child's needs and their own feelings toward him.

A brief synopsis of two case histories may show two kinds of aphasia in children.[10]

[9] Sheldon Rappaport, ed., *Childhood Aphasia and Brain Damage: A Definition*, Narberth, Pennsylvania: Livingston Publishing Company, 1963, p. 96.

[10] *Ibid.*, pp. 101–2, 104–6.

The first one described was the case of a six-year-old boy called Ted. He came to a children's clinic because he could not speak, had temper tantrums, showed separation anxiety over being removed from his mother, and inability to relate to most people. He began life in auspicious fashion, sitting up at six months, walking before his first birthday. When he was 16 months old, he fell down a flight of stairs; and although the pediatrician could find no damage, Ted refused to walk for ten days after the accident. At about two and a half years of age he began to talk but said only a few words. Instead of increasing his vocabulary, he soon lost all of his verbal communication and played quietly by himself.

When he was examined, he was found to be quite normal physically and to have good hearing. He tried to perform all testing tasks, both in speech and in nonlanguage activities. He could understand directions but became confused when multiple ones were given to him, such as, "Get the book from the case, put it by your tablet, and take out your pencil." He was able to identify pictures and to imitate some lip and tongue actions.

Ted was diagnosed as a child with dyspraxia, or expressive aphasia. He was placed in a remedial learning situation and after a semester had learned to read, speak, and write minimally. He could retain and recall material and made the progress expected of a child with good learning ability and at least normal intelligence.

Although he still has many difficulties in gross- and fine-motor activities, he has been able to learn such academic skills as writing and to acquire many of the physical skills learned by boys of his age. He still does not play easily in a group, but he is beginning to develop abilities to join in group play activities upon request.

Ted was a youngster with motor aphasia. A second case

history describes Al, an eleven-year-old with receptive aphasia. Al was a premature baby who weighed three and a half pounds at birth and who was jaundiced and placed in an incubator for a month. His developmental history was unremarkable. He sat up at seven months, walked at 15 months. He had no speech before the age of three, when an upper respiratory infection with high fever resulted in a convulsion and loss of consciousness.

On his psychological examinations Al's IQ scores ranged from 114 to 122. He showed a liking for music and at home enjoyed music on the radio. His response to sounds surrounding him was variable. For example, in class he might attend to the music of a piano coming from another room.

He was able to identify pictures of common objects through vision alone. He responded to his name and could add and subtract figures which did not involve borrowing or carrying. He did not show much understanding of speech but was able to grasp ideas which came to him from nonverbal means.

After he had been in a residential program for a year and a half, Al was able to read, say, and write from memory all of the material he had learned. By that time he had had well over 300 nouns, six structured sentences, and four prepositions.

As he progressed in his education, he began trying very hard to discriminate sentences spoken in a loud tone of voice from a distance of ten feet. However, because of his sensory difficulty, he had to have complete silence in order to discriminate accurately and had to concentrate very hard on the situation.

As can be seen from the two examples, Al and Ted were both diagnosed as aphasic children, but each of them manifested his problem in different areas. Ted's problems were in his motor activities, in movement, and in tasks requiring gross- and fine-motor skills. Al's were in his hearing and in his ability to discriminate sounds. Individual methods were needed for helping these two youngsters.

Brain Injury

What do we mean when we speak of brain injury? Who are the children with it, and how do they behave? To see the comprehensive nature of the term, Laura E. Lehtinen, clinical director of the Cove Schools, puts it this way:

> Brain injury is an all-inclusive term. If you will think of the pie-like diagrams with which statisticians describe our tax expenditures, we can picture what brain injury may mean. A good sized piece of this circle or pie—representing childhood brain injury—will consist of cerebral palsy. This is the brain injury that results in motor disability of varying kinds and degrees. Another segment will include the convulsive disorders resulting from brain injury. Still another piece, a large one, will represent mental retardation due to brain injury. A fourth piece represents the learning disabilities and behavior disorders resulting from brain injury. In children it is rare to find that any one of these conditions exists as an isolated disorder. Generally they overlap.

The psychologist then explains who the youngsters are:

> The problems of the group of brain-injured children with normal or close to normal intelligence but with learning disabilities, language and perceptual disturbances and behavior disorders are the ones of concern to us today . . . we will use the term, brain injury, and indicate with this the child who has little or no apparent motor deficit, who may or may not have seizures, whose intelligence is close to or actually within the normal range, who shows disturbances in behavior and emotional control and who has difficulties in learning based on perceptual, integrative, and associative dysfunction.[11]

[11] Laura E. Lehtinen, "The Brain-Injured Child: What Can We Do for Him?", Dallas, Texas: *The Dallas Medical Journal,* Special Edition, March 1959, p. 15.

This group of minimally brain-injured children often becomes more disadvantaged than the population of young people whose disability shows itself in physical ways, such as crippling or blindness or deafness. The very "unvisual" aspects of minimal brain injury and the fact that it is demonstrated in bizarre behavior and often in hyperactivity and distractibility make parents ignore or attempt to explain away the difficulty. It has been said that the minimally brain-injured child has been ignored by most groups; yet he is the one who is most likely to become a ward of the courts. Dr. Sheldon Rappaport states that this minimal disturbance is comparable to having something go wrong at the head of the Ford Motor Company's assembly line and throw all future operations out of kilter.

A professor of education and psychology of the University of Michigan, Dr. William M. Cruickshank, stated the emergence of the brain-injured child's problem in this way:

> Over the past thirty years, it is rare that the professions have been challenged to the degree they have been recently by a single type or group of problems such as are presented by the brain-injured child. The professions have been comfortable with the traditional classifications of disability: the deaf, the hard of hearing, the blind, the crippled, the mentally retarded, and others. . . . All of a sudden, into the relative calm of the traditional classifications of disability was thrust a different problem. Not new, but different, and one which the traditional concepts and classifications were not prepared to assimilate. Over the years there had always been some mentally retarded children who did not seem to fit the pattern of mental retardation. Always there were reports of emotionally disturbed children who did not respond to the therapies and educational programs to which the majority of the children in the respective classifications responded well . . .

Dr. Cruickshank tells some of the historical background of work with brain-injured young people:

It cannot be said that the problem of the brain-injured child is fully understood. This is a field of special education definitely in transition. More is now understood than is put into practice. Tens of thousands of brain-injured children wait for services which are still many years in the making. . . . An understanding based on some research and observation of methods of education of these children is in the literature, although a consensus as to method has not been fully achieved. The brain-injured child constitutes the frontier of special education.[12]

The complexity of the problem of definition, diagnosis, and prescription was set out by Dr. Herbert G. Birch at a conference in this way:

Given the complex matrix of behavioral disturbance which children designed as "brain damaged" present, it is clear that no single scientific discipline and no simple research strategy can possibly provide knowledge that will result in adequate understanding or effective planning for the children with whom we are concerned. To approach the problems meaningfully requires the pooled resources, skills, and techniques of, at the very least, such disciplines as neurology, psychology, physiology, psychiatry, education, epidemiology, sociology, pediatrics, and obstetrics. Working together these disciplines can approach the questions . . . which emerge in any serious consideration of children with brain injury.[13]

Thus, as in other disabilities with children, it is easy to recognize that the efforts of many disciplines and the understanding and cooperation of many people relating to the child must combine to help him become as achieving a person as is possible.

[12] William M. Cruickshank, "An Introductory Overview," in *The Teacher of Brain-Injured Children,* New York: Syracuse University Press, 1966, pp. 3, 4.

[13] Herbert G. Birch, *Brain Damage in Children,* Baltimore: The Williams and Wilkins Company, 1964, p. 11.

Since increasing efforts are being made toward working with the "areas of wellness" in even the sickest of people, programs have been directed toward strengthening the achieving portions of the brain-injured child's abilities.

The goals have been stated by a father in this way:

> To keep the child on the course which will eventually lead him to the goal achieved by the normal child, it is necessary that he use every faculty required for the mastery of a given skill, even though some faculties may be weak or inefficient. For the brain-injured child is a human being who is struggling to adjust to and assert himself in the world under a tremendous handicap. His potential is often greater than it seems, but his handicap is great too. His own efforts must not be discounted, for he, too, is battling against his handicap. Given proper help and direction many of these children can live a normal, useful life. That is the measure of victory of the human spirit over odds that at the outset may appear overwhelming.[14]

What are these brain-injured children like? How do they respond to people? Let us visit a small class of such children and see five of them seated around a table. Here is how the conversation goes:

"Does it have to be hot outside to snow?"

"No, Christmas."

"Around a birthday time, what is sweet?"

"An apple."

"What is the name of a flower, Betty?"

"Growing in the ground."

These responses have been elicited after much effort and are given by children who are being taught, slowly, repeatedly, carefully, to find some order in the universe, some way to manage themselves and the world in which they live.

[14] Richard S. Lewis, Alfred A. Strauss, and Laura E. Lehtinen, *The Other Child,* New York: Grune and Stratton, 1960, p. 139.

The search for an ordered universe. That is the task of the brain-injured child, whose emotions race through him like motion pictures at high speed, whose body is always on the move, who is distracted by everything and everybody.

BETTY

Look at Betty. A Hummel figure of a girl, dark hair swinging over her shoulders, hands like small white birds flying. As she lay in utero slumbering, were her dreams quiet ones and gentle? Did they lie softly as a whisper over her form? Or even then, within her mother's womb, was the damage there, making her restless, ever-moving, impatient for a life which in itself offered little that was quiet and placid?

For Betty, days are sequences of unrelated events, during which she tries to perform or react in ways that her parents wish her to do. But there seems to be a motor in her, one which is always turned on, always making her move from chair to floor to door to chair.

Betty, at five, remembers little of success. She tries to fathom the order of the world. Every day she makes the effort.

Some moments she is filled with a pain so deep she cannot move. Especially when she has made Mother unhappy. The hurt slices her and brings tears. But in a minute it is gone; and while Mother still looks at her sadly, she has grabbed her ball and started outside.

At other times she and Mommy and Daddy are in the front room, all together and happy. And even while they are smiling, she is overcome with sad feelings and begins to cry. Her crying always seems to be a surprise. And sometimes she starts to laugh and can't stop, and nobody laughs with her.

Betty's world is much mixed up.

When she goes out to play, Mother always stands nearby to watch. That is because cars have nearly hit her when she rushed into the street a couple of times, and the doctor had to set her arm when she fell out of the high tree in the yard.

It's nice to have friends, and Betty wishes that girls would play with her. Kathy used to, and so did Sue. But they don't like her now. She tried to play with them, but in a minute she got angry and hit them. And even though she got sorry fast, they did not come over to her yard any more.

Something is wrong. Betty knows it. And she wants to make it right. When Mother tells her to sit in a chair, she tries to do it, really tries. But then there is a noise at the window, or a bird flying by, or a leaf touching the pane, and she cannot stop herself from running over to look at them.

Or if Mother shows her a picture book, Betty wants to look at it. Mother points to a picture and says, "Betty, what is that?" And when Betty says, "That is a yellow flower," Mother gets upset and says, "Don't you see the house and the people and the blue sky and the car in the driveway? Don't you see?" Betty is very sad because she does not see. But the yellow flower is pretty.

And sometimes when she asks Mother a question, Mother says, "But you asked me that a minute ago. And this morning. And last night." Then Betty knows that she has made Mother unhappy, but she does not know how to stop.

When the noise begins, Betty feels as if booming airplanes are hitting at her. She has to cover her ears, and she begs for the noise to go away. When the television comes on, she covers her ears and begins to cry and scream, and she gets cold and wet and very scared. Then she starts to run around the room, and Mother and Daddy sometimes grab her by the shoulder and try to make her be still.

Betty would like to turn down that motor which keeps her on the move. She wishes that she could make herself like Kathy or like Sue. They always know what is Monday and when it is 11 o'clock or how soon Christmas will come or if it is summer. For them things are not always on the move— themselves, their room, the figures in a book.

Betty is more fortunate now than if she had been born a half century ago, for information about brain-injured children is growing in medical, psychological, and educational circles, and increasing knowledge about how such children can be helped is being utilized. Unfortunately, there has been a great delay in the past in recognizing that certain abnormal and antisocial behavior might be based on brain injury, even though there were not signs of paralysis or difficulty in walking.

What do we mean when we speak of brain injury? The immediate picture which comes to mind is that of a blow or lesion specifically to one area of the brain and one which causes certain kinds of behavior or reactions. Although not all types of brain injuries can be prevented, physicians recognize that oftentimes damage to the brain occurs just before, during, or just after birth. Premature babies are especially vulnerable. Many changes have been made in obstetrical practices to give the infant the maximum chance for respiration to begin promptly.

However, sometimes the injury which may happen to an infant comes long before birth and is caused by factors so subtle that they must be traced back as a detective would search for causes. The obvious effects of certain illnesses in the mother are widely known, but there are other actions which may also play their insidious and lasting parts.

KEITH

It is possible that Keith can attest to such facts. For Keith was diagnosed as a brain-injured child when he was five years old. Up to that time he had had almost no speech and no competence with printed symbols of any kind. "He will outgrow it," said the doctors until Keith's parents could no longer endure the knowledge that something was wrong and should be corrected. When the electroencephalogram demonstrated the brain damage in Keith, the attending physician asked his mother if she could recall anything in his prenatal life which might have affected him. As she tried to think back through the first trimester of her pregnancy, she recalled that she and Keith's father and another couple had taken a long drive into the mountains on one weekend. They had gone from the low altitude of their Texas home to a height of 12,000 feet. She explained to the doctor that they had remained at that altitude for only two hours and that she had not exerted herself during that period. The physician responded that the lack of oxygen at that high altitude could not be eliminated as a possible cause of Keith's brain damage, especially if no other causative factor could be found!

As Keith's father began to research into the area of brain damage, he discovered that the Indians had long known of the danger of high altitudes on infants. In fact, they would not permit children to be conceived at the mountain heights and would never let a pregnant woman stay on the mountain during the time of her pregnancy!

Other overt causes of brain damage in children are encephalitis, severe burns, and, of course, actual head injuries. Present methods of using antibiotics to lessen high fever in small children have also served to reduce brain damage following such illnesses. Often the injury did not manifest itself for some years but then could almost always be traced back to a severe illness with attendant extreme heights in temperature, as was the case with Kim.

DON

Take Don. Like Betty he would like to "belong" to a world where things are real and orderly. He is always upsetting his brother and his mother and daddy, and he does not always, or often, know why.

He is seven, and he has his own room—a nice room where he can sleep and be by himself. Mother comes from town and brings him something. She says, "Don, here is a car. Play with it." Don holds it in his hands. He does not know exactly what Mother means by "car." He sees some wheels, and they turn around. He begins to turn them, over and over and over and over. They go faster and still faster, and finally one falls off altogether. And then he sees a turning thing, and he begins to turn it and turn it and turn it and turn it, and soon it goes "sprong" and stops turning. Mother comes in, and she starts to yell. "Don, you've broken up the car I brought you. Five minutes, and it's broken to bits. What will I do with you?"

Don looks sadly at Mother. She brought him something to play with, and he has been playing. He runs his fingers up and down his legs. He is sorry to make Mother angry, but he does not know how to stop.

He remembers that he was downstairs with Mother and Daddy when some people came over. His nose was running, and Mother said, "Don, go upstairs and get a handkerchief out of your drawer." He went upstairs, as fast as he could run, and he pulled the drawers out of his dresser, all of them, until he found the one with the handkerchiefs, and he came downstairs with a lot of them in his hand. Mother looked sad or angry and very unhappy with him, and he was sorry.

It was the same way when all the family was going out to dinner. Mother asked him to get dressed so that they would be able to leave. And he did go upstairs to his nice room to start to dress. But when Mother came in and found him stacking blocks, she began to yell again and said, "Don, it was thirty minutes ago that I sent you upstairs. And you haven't even started. Haven't done a thing. What will I do with you?"

ESTHER

Esther, at twelve, is able to perceive the world in a clearer way than she could as a small child. In addition, she is able to look at her illness with a bit of perspective. But this has come about only after five years of residential care, where her schooling has been carefully structured and her living conditions supervised.

Esther remembers how it was. At home, with Tom and Louis and Elaine all playing together and laughing together and going out to shows or picnics, she felt left out, different, not wanted, broken. Esther remembers, painfully, the way it felt to be broken, not whole. And she could not tell anyone because she could not speak nor could she herself understand what was wrong except that she knew her differences. Where Tommy could make others laugh, she brought only frowns or scoldings. How could she transmit the feeling that the brokenness was in her heart and being and that when anything else broke, it was as if a piece of her were torn away? She would be in the car with Daddy; and if the car would not go, she would begin to cry and scream. And no one knew that the car's inability was hers too. If a glass shattered on the tile floor at home, she threw herself onto the same floor and wept without control. She could not tell others that it was she who was shredded into pieces on the tile and that she did not believe that anyone or anything could ever make her whole.

Esther is able to reflect because she is beginning to understand the forces which were at work within her. She is beginning to learn how to think through an idea, how to read words, how to know the world in its organization and wholeness.

She smiles because she recognizes that Daddy now also knows about the change in her. His understanding came about last week right after the big snow storm. Daddy asked her to go outside with him and to build a snowman. Esther and he worked for an hour, and Daddy was pleased to see how she could form a leg and an arm and the shape of a man.

They put the head on the snowman—he was almost as tall as Esther—and Daddy went inside to get an old straw hat. Esther stood back and surveyed the figure. It was a fine looking man. She and Daddy had done a good job. The sun sparkled on the snow, and Daddy came running down the front stairs, a very handsome man in his bright green jacket. Daddy put the straw hat on top of the snowman, and one half of the head came off and tumbled in the snow.

Esther felt the hurt of the old wound of brokenness. Then she saw Daddy's face—frightened and horrified. He looked at her, and she was able to muster her strength and to say, "Don't worry, Daddy. We'll fix it together. Let's put the head back on the snowman."

Daddy and she have been able to do a lot of things together since that day. Without many words she has been able to tell him that she remembers the brokenness and the pain but that she is able to move forward in a new way.

JUDY

Judy is another youngster who can verbalize the change which has happened to her after long months of treatment. One of twins, Judy spent her first two months in an incubator. She can remember isolated incidents from her early life, especially the temper which came like a storm and destroyed everything in its path. For her the world was indeed upside down and inside out. Everything was in pieces—words, scenes, music. Talk was garbled, sights without meaning, and she spent her days in a fragmented universe without direction or content.

Judy can now recall how it was, after she had been having careful treatment for many months, when she first saw her Mother—all of her. She did not know then why Mother cried when she said, "Mother, I can see you, every bit of you, all of your buttons, and your eyes and hair and shoes. Mother, I see you all the way." Judy remembers too that when she began to see her mother whole, she also started to see the wholeness of the entire world around her, and after a time she could see her own self in that world.

†   †   †

> Which is a "d" and which a "b"?
> Is this "saw" or is it "was"?
> What is sweet? What sour?
> What is up? And where is down?
> When is summer? And when spring?

Simple questions. Yet for the child with learning disabilities they are almost impossible to answer. In a universe which is in bits, the simple continuity of life and of life's tasks cannot be seen.

Many experts give many explanations concerning these children. There are theories of causation and differences concerning treatment. Yet all of those who work in a meaningful way with these young people recognize that no matter what the label, there are children who have problems in living. They recognize that behavior which may seem bizarre or out of context is, according to the child's view of himself and his world, perfectly appropriate. The experts who have been able to reach these children and to help them are the ones who can feel the pain and the rejection and the lack of wholeness which constitute much of the children's lives. They see the child, know his need, and work with him on the basis of his own competence.

They help him garner his own strengths and gain his own independence. Perhaps their philosophy was best expressed by a teacher in a class for brain-injured children. She had laid out a plank and was having the children develop their motor abilities by walking foot over foot across the plank. She stayed very close to the little boys, encouraged them softly as they walked. One plaid-shirted little fellow seemed unsure of his feet, and she walked beside him, close enough that he knew she was near, yet far enough that she did not touch him. What she said, softly, was,

"If you need help, hold out your hand."

CHAPTER III

PARENTS AND TEACHERS VIEW
THE DAMAGED CHILD
"No Magic Pill Exists"

EVERY WOMAN who carries a child within her also holds the vision of what he will be, the hopes of what he can be, the assurance of what he must be. The tiny fetus slumbering in utero symbolizes dreams unfulfilled and joys unknown. The potential father, too, greets with buoyancy and delight the thought of a son who will be a miniature form of all that the father wishes he might have been. A son! A young boy, sturdy, forthright. And, of course, smart and capable. A son to carry on the name and the tradition and the unique quality of a family. Or a daughter, petite and delectable. One who will adore her father and sit lovingly on his lap with her golden head against his shoulder.

Each parent knows that he will need to compromise his dream a bit. Children cry and become ill. Not all of them are handsome or beautiful. And some are smarter than others. Each parent has already "bargained" with himself and has settled on some possibilities less than perfection.

But no parent is prepared for the damaged child. Psychologists and psychiatrists know of the devastating gamut which parents run—from nonrecognition to fearful discovery to denial and back to some form of acceptance. The reactions of the parents, of course, vary with the severity of the disturbance in the child and the makeup of the parents themselves. It is interesting, however, that parents of children who have obvious and observable defects often are able to make a better adjustment to their problem than are the parents of a child with "hidden" defects. As is true with the seriously disturbed child, the one with brain damage may be mistaken for an un-disciplined, poorly trained, acting-out youngster. If he empties a flowerpot on the living room rug or pulls the knobs off the television set or scatters books across the room, any observer might comment, "What that child needs is a good hairbrush properly applied at the strategic spot."

And the parent who has to live with this hyperactive, constantly moving child, might well agree!

From a psychiatric point of view, what happens between a brain-damaged child and his parents is of major importance. Here is how psychiatrist Gerald H. J. Pearson describes it:

> As the child grows older, the parents start to worry and be-come more and more disappointed in him. They react to their disappointment and worry in different ways. Some deny their child's differences by thinking he is lazy or stubborn and must be forced to do things. Others pity and overprotect the child, while still others reject him in everything he does, because he is not like other children. His behavior hurts their pride, for to all parents the child is an extension of themselves. What-ever real love they have for the child becomes strangled by their negative feelings. As a result, the child grows up in an atmosphere lacking real love. That prevents him from making stable identifications with his parents . . . the parents are hurt by the child and dislike him, to which he reacts with resentment and antagonism. They, in turn, react against this, and a vicious circle ensues in parent-child relationship, which is understandable because even parents cannot suffer constant humiliation.[1]

Although Dr. Pearson is discussing an extreme in re-actions between parents and injured child, some of the com-

---

[1] Sheldon R. Rappaport, ed., *Childhood Aphasia and Brain Damage: A Definition,* Narberth, Pennsylvania: Livingston Publishing Company, 1963, p. 60.

ponent parts of the problem exist between any damaged child and his parents. We have seen, in the previous chapter, how the world looks to the child who is "not whole" and who is unable to perceive the world in its stable and orderly fashion. We know that he reacts in the best method he can and that what he does makes sense from his own viewpoint. We have recognized that, if we could understand the basic premise from which the injured child operates, we would find all that he does quite logical and in keeping with his concept of the world.

The child himself has the same needs and feelings as all children, but where the others succeed, he knows only failure. Each endeavor for him is another lesson in frustration, and he finds that he is fighting for a kind of survival from the moment he is born.

Now we shall see how some of this behavior must seem to the parents who are subjected to the eroding quality of the child's constant failure or lack of suitable responses—the parents whose dream of a child of strength and beauty has disappeared, a fog in the sunlight.

The Parents' View

Dr. Sheldon Rappaport of the Pathway School has described some of the interactions between mother and brain-damaged child. He stated that the child does not evoke the warm or pleasant responses generally related to motherhood. He does not "trigger" off normal mother response patterns, and she, in turn, is guilty because of her own reactions. The mother feels that she has not done anything to "deserve" such behavior, and she seeks help, first from her husband, who is generally of little assistance, and then from her pediatrician, who often tells her that the child will "outgrow it." The mother, having no one to support her and yet shredded by the behavior of the infant, deals with her mounting anxiety as best she can.

Most brain-injured children at first are hypoactive. They have difficulty in sucking; thus, feeding the infant becomes a long-term and major problem in itself. According to Dr. Rappaport, the mother is consumed with her own guilt feelings. She may react in one of two ways to the almost constant crying of the infant. She may "smother" him with attention but not really give him the kind of stimulus he needs. Or she may leave him in his bed and simply let him cry. Without professional guidance, she does not know how to stimulate him in a way that will aid his development and therefore help him to fill in appropriately and effectively those development gaps caused by his neurological difficulty.

This mother has many guilt feelings about her child; she suffers nightmares; she does not know how to find a way of living with this infant, who, after all, is part of herself and her husband, the child for whom she longed and dreamed.

Where is she to turn, and how can she find a way of regulating her life and that of the child?

The mother is knowing guilt, anger, and frustration; the child himself is reacting to the mother's feelings. He develops a negative attitude toward himself. The infant recognizes how the mother regards him; it is reflected in the way she handles and feeds him. She is communicating to him the true feelings she has, and no matter how hard she tries, she lets her child know that he is troublesome and unloved. And here, again, comes the circular pattern of mother's attitudes reflected in the child, who, like a mirror, gives back the image.

While these early infant days are difficult for the mother, they are only the beginning of days and weeks and years of total devastation during which the parents may struggle for actual survival and certainly for psychological life.

When the child reaches the age of one or two or three, he acts, as Dr. Rappaport says, as if he were "shot out of a gun." His hypoactivity changes to hyperactivity, and he cannot be stopped. During all of his early months he has had no gratification through his motor system. Finally he has learned to do some of the acts with his body that he has endeavored to do before. He can walk and run and climb and throw balls. Now he is on the go, but, again, he is a car without brakes, for he moves at a high rate of speed but without purpose or direction which is fathomable to the bewildered and distraught mother.

At this stage of his life the child may wake up at five in the morning. He springs out of bed and rushes into the kitchen. There he opens the cabinets and pulls out all of the pots and pans. He grabs a chair and brings it to the drainboard, where he finds the cans of coffee and flour and sugar. Very quickly he pulls them to the floor and turns them over in great heaps on the linoleum. It is now five fifteen. He moves from kitchen into living room and begins to swing from the drapes, pulling them in heaps over his head.

While he is destroying the peace of the household and bringing his mother to tears, this child still is endeavoring to find some manageable way to live. One writer describes him thus:

> He wants desperately to be accepted. He would gladly obey all the rules, if only he could. An uninhibited person is able to weigh the pros and cons of his actions, and deliberately chooses an eccentric pattern of behavior. The brain-injured child, with his faulty "checking" mechanism, cannot always control his impulses. He is highly emotional and often functions as though in a panic.
>
> The average uninhibited individual is able to perceive the reactions of society to his behavior, but he doesn't *choose*

to inhibit himself. With the brain-injured child, it is not a matter of choice; he *cannot* perceive the reaction of society to his behavior and *cannot* inhibit himself.[2]

Although the psychiatrist or educator may recognize that this child is fighting for psychic survival, the miserable mother can see only that she is housing a monster who cannot understand what she says or feels and who will not conform to any rule of the household.

The mother cannot bear the devastation wrought by this child. She punishes him, and he cannot understand why. Here a power struggle begins between mother and child. The child is endeavoring to grasp something about which he can feel good—his running, his climbing, his throwing. He discovers that his only success is in upsetting people, and a battle begins.

Unless some kind of intermediary help is brought to bear, the mother and child will wreak endless damage upon one another. And although it is easy to say and difficult to accomplish, the fact is that parents can help their brain-damaged child only when they begin to understand him. They need to know *why* he acts in the way he does.

The catastrophic collapse which many children with brain damage go through has often been likened to a temper tantrum, but it is far different. The child goes to pieces because suddenly the anger and frustration of being unable to cope with situations become overwhelming and rush over the child, a wild tide out of its banks. Anyone who has worked hours on a tedious task of putting together a watch or a piece of furniture knows the almost unbearable anger which accompanies a sudden snapping of the mechanism or breaking of the wood.

[2] Ernest Siegel, *Helping the Brain-Injured Child,* New York: Association for Brain-Injured Children, 1961, pp. 38, 39.

So it is with the brain-injured child. Despite the fact that the parents may not know what the buildup to the sudden sadness is, they can treat the collapse for what it is.

At such moments patient understanding on the part of parents will give the brain-injured child reassurance and will serve as the mortar to help cement the bricks of his ego-building.

Two Coping Families

Sometimes there are unusual parents, human beings with strength and insight and the ability to reach beyond themselves and to lead their children patiently into a land of living, feeling people. Such a parent was Barbara Trace, who, with Shulamith Kastein, has written *The Birth of Language* concerning her damaged and aphasic child. She says:

. . . For the most part, she cried and fussed, and seemed unable to derive any comfort from being held, caressed, or rocked. . . . Although this was markedly different from my experience with our two sons, I was not concerned at first. I was essentially relaxed and confident because I felt that I was an experienced and competent mother . . .

Still, as the months passed, I found that I was making no headway. I became more perplexed and harassed, but I was still not discouraged. It was obvious that Joan was not in contact with me or with her environment. I considered this to be a reflection of a slower maturing process, and expected her to calm down as soon as she could understand herself and her environment better. To this end, I provided her with a consistent routine, gentle loving care, a calm atmosphere, and abundant attention. I tried to define limits and administer necessary disciplines.

Joan was a restless, driven child involved largely in seemingly aimless, frustrating, destructive activity. She could not or would not accept limits. She did not respond to discipline.

. . . Her expression of her needs baffled me completely, and as a result, my interpretation of her wants usually was incorrect.

If Joan was thirsty, hungry, tired, yearning to go outdoors, or hurt, her problem remained locked within her. . . . Joan cried and waved her arms haphazardly all about her in a vain attempt to express herself, and she and I grew more and more frustrated because we simply did not understand each other . . .

Joan could not associate her need with the means of gratifying it even if the means of doing so were right before her. For instance, if she was thirsty, and there was a container of milk on the table, she could not point to it, touch it, take it . . .[3]

Because Joan was premature, Mrs. Trace had reason to accept many of the slow and difficult patterns of Joan's development. Nevertheless, awareness came in subtle ways and over a period of time. She says:

The realization of what was wrong came slowly, but at last, we acknowledged the fact that Joan had a calamitous deficiency. Until she was approximately three and one-half years old, she had practically no language comprehension. Not only was she not able to speak, but she appeared to be incapable of understanding concepts and words. She seemed unable to interpret gestures or to translate her own needs into gestures . . .[4]

Mrs. Trace describes some of the behavior of Joan toward her family and their own reactions toward her. She pinpoints the family situations in this way:

She did not, as yet, understand the most elementary meaning of relationship.

[3] Shulamith Kastein and Barbara Trace, *The Birth of Language,* Springfield, Illinois: Charles C Thomas, 1966, pp. 28, 29.

[4] *Ibid.,* p. 38.

. . . She did not seem to know who her father and I were. Certainly, we were important to her, but not as people. We were merely familiar structures like her bed or her play table that she clung to for her very existence. She expressed panic when either her father or I, depending upon who was caring for her at the time, disappeared even momentarily from her view. She showed no capacity for accepting or giving love . . .[5]

The laborious teaching process which parents go through to help their damaged children may best be described by Mrs. Trace:

At first Joan needed help in becoming aware of herself before she could relate to and eventually communicate with those around her. She had to learn to feel, look, and listen. She had to be taught the meaning of each word. Everything had to be reduced to its simplest and most concrete denominator before she could comprehend it. Language had to be fed slowly and built step by step and slowly, over the years, the chain of development, broken in so many places at first, was restored.[6]

A picture book for parents once showed a mother standing with her arms out to her side and a child growing from the arm. The caption read, "We think of children as extensions of ourselves." Although the cartoon was meant for humor, the truth is that parents regard a failure on the part of their children as a double failure—that of themselves as parents and that of "their own extensions." It is difficult for many parents to erase the sense of failure and to look squarely at the problem which the child himself is facing.

As we have seen, a stable family may be able to "absorb" the damaged child and to help him to achieve to his full capabilities. Let us look at a second such family. Take Joel, for

[5] *Ibid.,* p. 35.
[6] *Ibid.,* p. 16.

instance. Joel was the fifth child in a family. His four pred-
ecessors were bright, extra-bright, robust, energetic. The old-
est, a tall genius of a boy, was almost ready for junior high
school. The second, another boy, headed his class, and the
next, a girl, was an "A" student in the third grade. Even preschool Betsy showed aptitude for everything she did.

And then came Joel. The physician's observation over several months caused him to tell the parents, "There is something wrong with this baby."

The parents had noted Joel's wide-apart eyes and button
nose. Nothing seemed wrong to them.

The pediatrician who examined Joel gave him a good
report. "He's fine." A second pediatrician confirmed the first.
The Johnsons tucked away the vague fear and memory of the
obstetrician's statement and enjoyed Joel in their family.

Joel was a little slow in sitting up, even slower in walking.
But then, as physicians and friends said frequently, "He'll
catch up." And when Joel's speech was much delayed, they
retorted with, "When he starts talking, he'll go so fast and
talk so much you'll wish he hadn't begun." By the time he was
two, Joel could say a few words. Mostly he opened those
wide-apart blue eyes and grunted or gestured for what he
wanted. And of course there were two big brothers and two
sisters to get it for him.

Mr. and Mrs. Johnson knew that Joel was different; yet
his differences did not seem alarming. As an infant, he was
placid and appealing. He laughed readily and played with his
brothers and sisters. And, as Mrs. Johnson put it, "We knew
that we were capable parents. We had four achieving and fine
youngsters. Our family relations were good, and somehow,
we felt, we would be able to do well for Joel."

A happy home life was not enough, however, when Joel
reached the age of four and was still all but speechless. Other

children noticed the difference; Joel began having trouble with his peers. Then the Johnsons took action.

First they made an appointment at the local guidance center. Although they had to wait for six months, results were helpful once the child psychiatrist saw them and began the testing.

"There is nothing more important than the diagnosis," Mr. and Mrs. Johnson state. "Nothing can help the child more than having an objective attitude in seeking medical and professional help and guidance or in seeking a medical and psychological inventory of the child."

The differential diagnosis made at the guidance center eliminated, one by one, possible causes of Joel's slow speech. He was not retarded, although his IQ in the 80's showed him much slower than his brothers and sisters. He was not deaf. He did not show emotional instability. More testing was done. Joel was diagnosed as aphasic.

"The diagnosis was the turning point," say the Johnsons. Joel was immediately put under the supervision of a speech therapist at a nearby university. In 16 months he had a vocabulary of 800 to 900 words. Then Joel went into the first grade, where the teachers rated him as "immature" or "very slow." He had toilet accidents. He did not show reading readiness. Something more had to be done.

Mr. Johnson, a chemist, did not waste time on recriminations nor on unproductive emotional reactions. He knew how to make decisions and how to arrive at useful solutions. He urged Mrs. Johnson to learn what she could both about aphasia and about treatment programs. She complied, and they were able to find another diagnostic clinic for learning problems close by.

At this clinic they were shown some of Joel's characteristics which gave evidence of neurological damage done during the first trimester of pregnancy. His wide-apart eyes and tiny nose were part of the evidence. So were the shape of his ears and his stubby fingers and "different" toes. When Joel was given an electroencephalogram at the clinic, it was discovered that, although he did not have convulsions overtly, numerous "short circuits" were occurring inside his brain. Joel was put on anticonvulsive medication.

Although Joel had to repeat the first grade, he found acceptance and companionship within his romping family, and he was able to maintain his happy outlook for the first few years of schooling. However, the Johnsons knew that more help was needed, and they found it in an interesting program at a nearby college. Here an intensive all-morning program went on every day throughout the summer. A maximum of five children were in each class, and teachers rotated every thirty minutes. Each child had a one-to-one contact with a teacher twice during the morning.

Equally as interesting as what went on with the children was what happened to the mothers who brought them there. Mothers were required to attend classes. They were also put into learning situations to find out about their own children. Each mother audited or took for credit a course in special education. The mother groups met together after the classes, and they exchanged reports on reading they had done. Bibliographies were prepared, and content was discussed. In addition, group sessions were held, with one of the teachers in charge, and here the mothers were able to talk about how it felt to be the parent of a damaged child and what the special problems were that presented themselves.

Events were used as the focal point for discussion. For example, one of the newspapers planned a feature series on the school program. A photographer took pictures of the children in various groups. No one objected except one mother.

She was furious that her child in a class for "special" children should have been photographed. Instead of bypassing the mother's anger, the group met together in the presence of the mother to discuss her indignation and what it represented. They were able to talk about the hurt and bewilderment which parents feel over having a child with disabilities and were also able to pursue the idea of how attitudes are formed and changed. Even though the mother did not participate in the discussion itself, she was able gradually to gain insights into her own feelings and what they represented.

Joel progressed fairly steadily until the fourth grade. After he had repeated it, his emotional problems increased. "I hate school!" he would say in his telegraphic type of speech. Or, bypassing verbs completely, he would cry, "Teacher no good." He began to have nightmares, and the next IQ test he had showed that his quotient had gone down by more than 10 points.

Once again Mr. and Mrs. Johnson looked to possibilities for Joel and finally found them in a small school in the town where the therapist lived. Joel began to commute by bus each day and to have therapy several times a week. He continued this school pattern until he reached high school age.

Now Joel is in high school, still having learning difficulties, but progressing in a program of distributive education. Perhaps he will be able to attend some nondemanding vocational junior college, where he will be able to increase his social and scholastic skills without meeting again the overpowering tide of failure.

The Johnson family is intact. If anything, it is closer than ever. There were times when the other children resented Joel, particularly when his schooling or therapy programs took many mother-hours from them. However, they exhibited the compassion which children often have for creatures less capable than themselves, and they all learned to give help to Joel when he needed it. Only the last sibling, three years Joel's junior, was slower to accept or to understand Joel's special needs.

Perhaps the reason for the family success might be summed up by Mrs. Johnson, who says, "All of the time that we were struggling to get Joel into a program suitable for himself, we were thankful for the other children we had. We knew that as parents we were capable and competent. I kept thinking of how it must be for parents whose first child was damaged. It would be more difficult for them to know that the fault did not lie with them. They would have to fight with their feelings of uncertainty and inadequacy.

"Even when I was pregnant with our sixth child, I did not have fears that she would be brain-damaged or that she would resemble Joel. After all, my first four had been extremely healthy and achieving, and I was confident that the sixth would be too."

Finally, however, Mrs. Johnson stated the important elements for successful coping. "First," she stated, "there must be recognition and acceptance. And then there has to be cooperation between the parents."

The two families whom we have just seen have coped successfully with the problems posed by their damaged children. They were unusual families. They had the means, the insights, the assets to help them deal with difficulties. The combination of resources—internal and external—gave them the ability to work effectively in a situation which, to many, would be insurmountable.

Not everyone can measure himself with the Johnson or the Trace families. The special situations or needs within other families may make such coping close to impossible.

However, within the mechanisms set up by the Johnsons

and the Traces are guidelines which might be followed in part and which might prove helpful to any family trying to deal with the difficulties presented by the damaged youngster.

Let us now look at two families who were not able to deal so skillfully with the problem.

Two Damaged Families

Helen Farnsworth was not so lucky. Her Janelle was brain-damaged in much the same way as Joel. But in this instance the edge of recrimination cut against both Helen and her husband, and by the time Janelle was twelve, the Farnsworths were separated and on their way to divorce.

Janelle's problem was not pinpointed until she had been in school for two years. Janelle, who could make shambles of the family apartment by the time she left for school, was able to mobilize herself to be quiet at kindergarten and in the first grade. There her blue eyes were fastened to her book, and she was able to use all of her energies toward conformity.

For Helen Farnsworth there was the lonely job of trying to understand what was happening to her slim young daughter, what was occurring in her marriage, and what she could do to maintain a semblance of sanity. There were days and weeks and even years of frantic uncertainty and of endeavors to meet one day or one hour in the best way that she could.

By the time Janelle's difficulty had been diagnosed and a special program found for her, Jim Farnsworth had left.

More subtle is the problem of the Lang family, where Timmy's dysfunction has caused a slow settling of the foundation of the Lang marriage and its stability. Lou and Janice Lang could not endure the thought of a child who was less than a model. Both of them had graduated from college with top honors (Lou was Phi Beta Kappa). Janice had always been in leading sorority and civic groups, and the two of them had decided while they were still engaged that their children would have a special place in the community where they lived. The niche they had envisioned was not exactly what was needed for Timmy. They did not want to be part of special education programs or parent groups or recreation marked for the handicapped. Not Janice and Lou! Thus, while Timmy continued to jump off anything—the roof of the house, the top of a car, a tree—while he repeated over and over and over any activity which caught his fancy, while he touched everyone and everything as if his fingers could transmit to him the meaning his mind could not grasp, while all of these things were happening to Timmy, Lou began to drink more and more and still more. He stayed away from home later in the evening, and he drank when he got there. And Janice started spending her daily hours at the hairdresser's or the luncheon table or at the country club.

Timmy was left in limbo, and Lou and Janice wandered their lonely paths away from him and from one another. Let another parent tell how it is:

> The dawning awareness that their child is different may involve an intense emotional experience for the parents. Many parents have told us that they reacted initially to the behavior aberrations of the child with feelings of humiliation, frustration, inadequacy, and despair. In this frame of mind, they could do little to help the child and feared that inadvertently they may have done much to disturb his behavior further by communicating their anxiety to him. It is inevitable that parents should be disturbed when the child is disturbed and that they should feed back to him their disturbance and further increase his. If this cycle is to be broken, the parents must be the ones to break it.[7]

[7] Richard S. Lewis, Alfred A. Strauss, and Laura E. Lehtinen, *The Other Child,* New York: Grune and Stratton, 1960, p. 9.

As we have seen, in some instances the family falls apart when there is a deviant child. Mutual recriminations come between husband and wife, blame about heredity and even environment. "Your uncle Bascomb always seemed a bit queer to me." "What about your Aunt Tilly? She couldn't even get out of high school." And as the parents take out their feelings of grief and frustration on one another, they add the pain of separation to the misery of their parenthood.

Sometimes the slowly corroding problem of having the child whose disability is not readily discernible but who is not able to fit into a regular school program may, in its own way, have as deleterious an effect on the parents as that of the obviously damaged child. The very "unvisual" quality of the difficulty of the child with minimal brain dysfunction makes him the target for criticism by parents and by teachers. Parents themselves feel a vague sense of dissatisfaction, a knowledge that they are not motivating their child enough, or they are not inspiring him properly, or they are not disciplining him frequently enough. Sometimes parents try the various techniques in rotating order, always with the same lack of success.

The child who is deviant, who does not give the satisfactions which other children give, who cannot respond in meaningful ways to his parents or his peers, is often difficult to love. Parents who have learned to adjust to the handicap and to their own feelings about that handicap are able to reach out to the child and to be supportive and loving and helpful. In speaking of the brain-injured child, Ernest Siegel puts it thus:

> The brain-injured child will incur reverses in his adventures outside of the home, but if his parents can give him the love, understanding, patience, and effective guidance that he so greatly needs, the home can become his sanctuary—the place where he can relax, meditate, and find strength to face a

world which finds him baffling and which he, in turn, finds so difficult to organize and comprehend.[8]

Finding the techniques of how to change the devastating cycle of defeat and misery requires many patient parent-hours. Mrs. Johnson had the benefit of counselors who were able to assist her and other mothers. Helen Farnsworth found her way eventually by helping to organize a parents' group in her city. Other families have enlisted the aid of friends or church. For each family the way to normalcy is individual and dependent on the makeup of the family itself and of the community in which they live.

Some Guidelines for Parents

It is vital that parents be able to regard the child first and the handicap second and to be able to see the young person as a human being with all of the human needs for love and acceptance and symbols of friendship.

Some young couples can find help through talking with professional counselors; others can learn acceptance through the efforts of ministers or friends. Many have learned new ways of coping by joining groups of parents who share the same problems.

Ray H. Barsch, professor of special education, Southern Connecticut State College, has pointed out that the parents of the damaged child have the same needs as the parents of normal children to transmit the culture and to help the child become an acceptable member of society. But he adds that too many professional persons give the parents a feeling that their problems are not of major concern and that their personal difficulties are not paramount. Dr. Barsch says, "Those who work with the parents should be able vicariously to experience

[8] Siegel, *op. cit.,* p. 45.

the strength and nature of their frustrations while at the same time structuring the relationship so as to facilitate change in parent attitudes and practice. If we feel an obligation to the exceptional child, it is hard to justify the lack of feeling of obligation toward the parents."[9]

Dr. Barsch described a program of group discussions for mothers of children with organic damage. The sessions were based on observations made in a careful training experiment on children with organic difficulties. In this demonstration the behavior and the needs of the children were observed and cataloged in order that parents could be helped in the day-by-day care for the young people.

Concerns of the parents were dealt with in these sessions, which were held on a continuous basis from September to June. Eight to ten mothers were in each group and no more than six couples in the parents' gatherings. Five or six such groups were formed and maintained each year.

A unique feature of these sessions is that the counselors (psychologists and social workers) related directly to the parents. They served as instructors of the parents in the same way that teachers served as instructors of the children. The program proved to be supportive and helpful. It gave reinforcement and aid to parents who could talk about actual home situations, such as discipline, eating problems, management of self-help skills, and other disturbing aspects of the child and family interrelationship. In fact, the meetings proved to be so meaningful to the parents themselves that several of the groups continued on their own basis after the formal program was concluded and met and preserved their identity for two to three years.

The results of seven years of such group process are help-

---

[9] Ray H. Barsch, "Counseling the Parent of the Brain-Damaged Child," in *Journal of Rehabilitation,* Vol. XXVII, No. 3, 1961, p. 1.

ful. Some parents, like the Johnsons, have been able to reach the maturity stage in their relationships with their child without a great deal of outside aid. Others, like the Farnsworths, were not. Dr. Barsch states that experiences with 38 groups over a seven-year period brought the following facts to light:

All parents start the group process at an *information-seeking* level. They want to ask questions and receive direct and specific answers. They want to know what to do, how to do it, and when.

This first stage gradually gives way to a *sharing* process in which they try to help each other by citing their own successes or failures, and discuss each other's specific problems in terms of "Why don't you try this?"

This sharing stage, which operates specifically in the area of technique, gradually gives way to the *feeling* stage in which they help each other to examine their own feelings about their child's behavior and to see how their own motivations, tensions, and attitudes are reflected in their child's behavior.

From this stage, they move into the *generalization* process in which they begin to consider the dynamics of child development and parental relationships for their other children as well.

The parents finally arrive at a *maturity* stage in which they integrate their brain-injured child into their total family unit and deal effectively with his problems because they understand the complexities of his development, and learn guiding principles to apply to their family relationships.[10]

Probably one of the most helpful aspects of such group discussions, in addition to the sharing of problems, is the way in which parents learn to look at normal child development and at the needs of all children. They also gain confidence in such discussions in their own capabilities as parents (and this,

[10] *Ibid.,* p. 3.

of course, is easier if they have already succeeded, as Mrs. Johnson had, as parents of "normal" children). They learn to set limits and to help their damaged children get ready for new experiences. They discover that they are the prime factors in being able to organize the child's world for him, and they gain insight into techniques for such planning. Most important, they begin to have confidence in themselves as parents and as human beings, and they then become able to cope with increased strength and understanding with many of the problems attendant to having a damaged child.

The enlarged concern for and by parents may be demonstrated by the attendance at meetings of the Association for Children with Learning Disabilities. The third annual conference in Tulsa brought more than 2,000 people instead of the expected 1,000. The fourth annual conference in New York in 1967 was set up for 2,500. Instead, around 5,000 people, primarily parents, attended the meetings and participated in the discussions.

At one of the sessions on "Developing the Child's Self-Management Skills," parents were vocal in stating that in too many instances there was no place for a father or mother to go to find out what was wrong with his child. After the first shock and groping, there is great need for a short cut to the heart of the diagnosis.

For too many parents, as is demonstrated by their descriptions, there are months and often years of uncertainty, of inability to grasp what is wrong with their child, to know how to handle a catastrophic collapse. (Is it a temper tantrum? Should I spank and punish? What brought it on?) Even for parents who have had other children, the knowledge that this child is in too many ways different from the others can soon make conscious a small fear which has been smoldering silently for some time.

The question which parents frequently ask, then, is whether or not there are guidelines to help direct them in their care for this child with learning disorders. Although there is no general prescription which can be written out, there are adaptable rules which will aid parents in their search for a way of living with this "special" child. A team of experts has laid out some rules for parents of children with reading disabilities. The thoughtful rules and suggestions listed in *Helping Children with Reading Disability* by Ruth B. Edgington may be adapted by parents.

Your own efforts to understand, to accept, and to help your own child control his behavior are sensed by him and will do much to relieve his anxiety and insecurity. Good effort should be praised, and successful work should be enjoyed and appreciated by his parents as well as by others who understand his problems. Some reward, such as putting a star on the work of a younger child or displaying the work of an older child, should follow his best efforts. Remember, the child keenly wants his work to be right, and he wants to be successful in your eyes as well as in his own.

One can expect great variability in the child's day-to-day performance. A bit of knowledge or skill apparently mastered one day, may be completely strange to the child the following day. Over a period of several days the child may be alert, cooperative, and able; the next day he may be clumsy, listless, and unable to learn. Even a youngster who is usually good-natured will occasionally be irritable, destructive, and unapproachable.

Reasons for this day-to-day variability are usually found in two main sources. First, the child is extremely responsive to his surroundings, such as events at home and disagreements with other children. Changing weather is quickly reflected in his school work and behavior. Second, the frustration felt by the child in his own "forgetting" from lesson to lesson, can be very disturbing and embarrassing to him unless this problem is tactfully managed.

One problem that will bother your child is the repetition of an error which he makes. When he is trying to correct himself, he will keep on making the same error. This may occur in reading, spelling, arithmetic, or writing, even when he is repeatedly reminded of what is right. To help him, quietly substitute another activity, or suggest that he come back to that work later, and go on to the next word or problem. After a brief time he can return to the troublesome work that he had to leave out.

Your child will be upset by work that seems to him to be too difficult, and he feels threatened with failure. The child will sometimes burst into tears. He feels helplessness, despair, and resentment toward you for demanding more than he can give. Here, work should stop completely, and the child should be soothed and "mothered." Work should not be resumed until he is over his unhappiness, and he is ready to learn. New work should not be taught when the child is upset: but review work, in which you know that he can be successful, should be done. From this successful level, build slowly and carefully through many different experiences, at the same degree of difficulty. Then the next material which was frustrating earlier may again be presented.

Other things may upset the child. Noises, movement, unrelated objects (pictures, calendars, flowers, toys, magazines, knick-knacks, ashtrays, etc.), "busy" wallpaper or windows may be distracting to your child as he tries to concentrate. Even the clothes which you and he will wear during his study time should not be new, or be distracting in color, design, or decoration. In other words, the clothes you wear should be familiar to him, or quiet color and design without decorative buttons or jewelry. His clothes should be simple and without details which remind him of play.

Also distracting are the demands of modern day living that result in tension and frustration for children and adults, alike.

Many children are already "driven" children because of their nervous energy which they have trouble controlling. Short periods of relaxation are vital for children who have problems.

A short relaxation activity after a period of concentrated effort often assists the child to be able to again concentrate. The form of this activity will have to be what best fits your child. Short and frequent activity games are better than just telling him to relax. During these activity times, *you* must also relax as *you* transmit, unconsciously, your own feelings of tension or calmness to him.

The Study Period

When selecting an hour of the day for your child's study period, many things should be considered. Who is to do the tutoring? In many communities a tutor might not be available. A parent may need to be the tutor. In some families a very responsible older child may be the only person with time available and therefore, may substitute for the parent. At what time is the parent available for teaching the child? The time for the study period should be arranged so that the person teaching the child can give him undivided attention. What is the age of the child, and how long is his attention span? Generally, the younger the child, the shorter the study period may need to be. Your child's attention span may be so short that two or three shorter periods will be more satisfactory than a single long period. When does the child feel freshest and most alert? Your child will perform best when feeling fresh and alert. If he is on medication, consider the influence of this on his alertness. You will want him to study during his "premium" time. Whatever time is decided upon, it should always be the same, because he will find security in a set routine.

Find a place for the child and the person who will teach him that is quiet and away from as many distractions as possible, such as noises, passing cars, radio, television, and playmates. Remove pictures, calendars, and toys from sight. In this place have a table or desk for the study time together. The surface of the desk should be clear, with only what is going to be used for each part of the period in reach or sight. Other articles needed later, may be placed on a convenient chair or box out of sight. Set aside this desk or table for study only. The child should not read, draw, or play games here at other times. Thus his mind will be helped to start work when seated there.

The parent will need to have a time to plan what work he will cover and what materials should be on hand when the study period comes. During the planning period is a good time in which to correct the work of the previous period rather than doing so during the study period as it will distract the child. Vary lessons by alternating reading with parts of the work which will require writing or drawing.

A cheerful, friendly, and helpful attitude will lead your child to look forward to these times when he can sit close to you and have you all to himself as he works. Putting your arm around his chair often helps to calm and reassure him. If he wants to get off the subject and talk about something else, make a written note of the topic, and tell him that you will talk with him about that after he finishes the task in hand. Do not neglect to do as you promised.

The more mature or the teen-age child, will, during the school year, need not only remedial work but also need to keep up his classwork as well as he can. He should be encouraged to do all that he can for himself. . . .

In general, your child's remedial work should include phonics practice, reading, spelling practice, and the use of written language. Include also activities for hand and eye coordination and for relaxation and puzzles or similar games to help him organize parts into whole ideas or to generalize what he knows. One well-planned hour, whether in a single block of time or divided into shorter periods, will be sufficient. Younger children may need the time divided. Allow about a half hour for phonics and reading, including a relaxation exercise. About twenty minutes should be spent on spelling practice and written language. The remaining time can be spent in organization of ideas and hand and eye coordination. For the older child or teen-ager, the order of activities may be different. It is suggested that the phonics and reading lesson should have a third to a half of the time allotted for the study period.[11]

A well-known authority in the area of minimal brain dysfunction, Dr. Sam D. Clements, Director of the Child Guidance Study Unit at the University of Arkansas Medical Center in Little Rock, reminds us that:

The important thing to remember is that so much of the irregular, and often irritating behavior is beyond the control of the child. The knowledge that the youngster is not merely being "hard-headed," rebellious, and uncooperative can produce positive changes in attitude toward the child, which of course, is of paramount importance if the overall therapeutic program is to produce maximum results.

The home management plan usually centers around an environment which is as free from extraneous stimulation as is reasonably possible. The environment should be simplified and structured in such a way as to produce a predictable, regimented, consistent everyday life pattern for the child, considering such features as:

1. A consistent "wake-up" time each morning.
2. Regulated bed-time and nap-time (when appropriate).
3. Meals to be served at the same time each day.
4. The child's regular activities should be on a time-table schedule, i.e., a specific and consistent time for play, watching television, homework and study, chores, etc.

With such a program, the child will learn what to expect and his habit formation tends to become self-regulating. Such routinization becomes a stabilizing influence for the child.

[11] Ruth B. Edgington, *Helping Children with Reading Disability*, Chicago: Developmental Learning Materials, 1968, pp. 8–11.

The child should be prepared for any change in schedule as it becomes necessary, but avoid telling him too far in advance if he is a child who tends to become disorganized with anticipation of an upcoming event. In general terms, one should:

1. Explain (but do not detail) the reasons for the change in schedule for that day.
2. If a trip or visit is involved, relate the purpose, approximate length of stay, and briefly describe the physical surroundings.
3. Let the child help in the preparations, i.e., packing his things, making out the grocery list, fixing food for a picnic, etc.

Ideally, the child should have a *quiet* room of his own, or at least a part of one screened off if he is of school age, to help control the effects of over-stimulation. Special features of the room should include:

1. Simplified decor, with calm, solid colors (pastel blues, greens, or neutral beige).
2. Room should be as free as possible from distracting stimuli such as mirrors, pictures, etc.
3. The child's study desk and/or play-work table should be located away from distracting elements such as windows, play equipments, etc. This can be achieved by placing the desk in front of a blank wall so that the rest of the room will be behind the child.
4. Toys, hobby equipment, etc., should be kept out of sight when not in use. A cabinet with shelves and doors can be used for this purpose.

Discipline

The major purpose of discipline is to mold or pattern the behavior of the child to prepare him for living in our society based on the required standards for success and acceptance. In this regard, the rules of expected behavior should be simple, definite, and consistent from one parent to the other.

The behavioral limits within which the child is expected to operate must be clearly communicated to him by both parents. The following general rules seem to work well with most M.B.D. children. They should be modified, however, to fit the individual child and the family living situation:

1. Do not punish the child for behavior he cannot help or control, such as, clumsiness, hyperactivity, short attention span, reading disability, etc.
2. Be *consistent* in behavioral demands. Both parents *must* agree on rules of conduct, and the punishment for breaking such rules. The child will tend to become "patterned" when he knows exactly what is expected of him.
3. Punishment should be designed to fit the child and to vary with the offense. The withholding of desired privileges and/or short-term isolation from family activities have proven to be effective. The cardinal rule is to "punish the *behavior* and not the child."
4. Punishment should follow immediately after the offense, so that the association between the undesirable behavior and the punishment which follows such action will be strengthened.
5. Punishment should be of short duration.
6. Rewarding the child for accomplishments and other forms of desired behavior is of equal importance for the patterning of the child. As with punishment, reward must be designed to fit the particular child and family "style." Verbal recognition and praise is often as ego-building as special privileges, monetary reward, or gifts.

Independence Training

The parents (and teachers) must recognize the M.B.D. child's prolonged need for direction and guidance, therefore dependence. However, social independence and the assumption of responsibilities should always be encouraged and fostered.

1. Daily or weekly chores around the home should be

included, even though the "quality" of the work may not satisfy the parents, e.g., picking up his own room, kitchen duties, yard duties, etc.

2. Encourage any special interest or talent which the child displays, e.g., sports, art work, hobbies, etc.

3. Encourage social activities with other children. If necessary, parents should seek out suitable playmates, and be willing to use the home as an "activity center." If a child is hyperactive, only one or possibly two playmates at a time may be best, with parents taking more supervisory role than would be necessary for children who are not handicapped by M.B.D.

4. Independence training should be extended to all social spheres and activities as the child becomes able to handle them. Included would be such self-care activities as personal hygiene, selection of clothes to wear, dressing, going to school alone, handling money, purchasing items from stores, running errands, initiating own play activities, etc.[12]

The Teacher's Dilemma

In towns and cities where there are no special education classes or where a child's difficulties have not been diagnosed, the teacher faces a classroom of first-graders and tries to analyze the different children. During the ensuing weeks she grows increasingly impatient with Freddy, who is constantly on the move, who cannot stay in his seat, who rushes from task to task and completes none of them. She may feel a bit of pity for Hilda, whose attempts at drawing or tracing are far below her age level. She may note that Frank can manipulate

[12] Sam D. Clements, *Some Aspects of the Characteristics, Management and Education of the Child With Minimal Brain Dysfunction,* England, Arkansas: Arkansas Association for Children with Learning Disabilities, Inc., and Glen Ellyn, Illinois: West Suburban Association for the Other Child, Inc., pp. 43–48, 60–64.

blocks and do fairly complicated tasks with his hands but is totally unable to repeat the verses the other children learn by ear.

Miss Franklin, the teacher, has neither the time nor the competence to sort out those children who are retarded from those who have emotional problems or from those with learning disabilities. She has been assigned a classroom full of lively first-grade children. She stands before the room and sighs a little, wishing that all of them were like pert little Millie, who is always freshly dressed, alert, and able to do any assignment given her.

No one blames Miss Franklin. She is but one person, and her job is to teach the largest number of children she can in the best manner possible. However, such recognition does not negate the necessity to locate the children with learning disabilities and to find the best means of helping them.

Some Guidelines for Teachers

One of the pioneers in working with children with minimal brain injury is Laura E. Lehtinen, who, with pioneer authority Dr. Alfred A. Strauss, was deeply concerned about brain-injured children more than twenty years ago. After outlining the kind of educational program needed for children with brain injury, she sets out some practical ways in which such a program works:

> Learning any of the scholastic skills requires that a certain minimum level of perceptual organization, concepts and memory has been attained. Since the child typically develops unevenly with considerable disparity between various mental abilities some faculties which are important for a skill such as reading may develop well in advance of others. Thus a child may be well qualified from the standpoint of vocabulary, concepts and memory to progress in reading but poorly qualified

in terms of the visual perceptual skills required. For such a child it is possible to prepare the learning situation in such a way that his poor visual perceptual skills do not block his progress unduly or result in confusions. For him the teacher would reduce the perceptual problems by heightening the stimulus value of the visual perceptual elements of the reading task. She might use color to differentiate parts of letters or words or emphasize them with heavy black outlines or remove portions of the material from their surroundings as in the study of words isolated from the book. She would also structure the visual space involved in the task by blocking some of it off with a mask or separating parts of it with colored or dark lines as on a workbook page. She would present a small enough amount at a time so that the child would not become confused by what could be for him a vast quantity of material. This type of structuring of visual space and emphasizing certain aspects of the visual stimulus may prove to be necessary in any academic area, not only reading. Using color to structure space can be used for the child who can form letters but cannot keep them on the line, for the child who can multiply but who becomes confused as to where to put the products, for the child who can write but cannot organize his work acceptably on a page, and so on.

For the child with auditory perceptual weaknesses the teacher would also strengthen the stimulus to make it more readily perceptible. She would speak more slowly, in shorter sentences and articulate carefully. She would be certain to have the child's full attention. She would be careful to check word meanings. The teaching of phonics would be preceded by much practice in auditory discrimination of sounds and analysis of the word parts to develop the minimum level of perceptual discrimination required for this aspect of reading.

In teaching any child with an impairment in one perceptual field the input must be supplemented through use of a more intact field. For the visually perceptually impaired child, verbally describing the visual percept or tracing it kinesthetically with the finger or eyes will hold attention on its important features and will improve the visual definition or articulation of the percept. For the child with auditory perceptual problems input supplementation can be achieved through visual and kinesthetic support. The teacher writes the word for the child to see, diagrams verbal concepts or relates words to visual and concrete models.

A good part of the task of leading the child toward independence of effort is to make him aware of how such supplementation can be helpful so that he can take over for himself. The child with visual perceptual difficulties can be taught to talk to himself about a task which has many visual perceptual demands; the child with auditory perceptual weaknesses can be taught to request spelling or to try to make the material visual. These children can and need to develop their own compensatory ways of studying if they are going to progress into higher grades on their own power.

As a result of our experience we have come to feel that the several academic skills make critical demands on certain mental abilities and less distinct demands on others. In reading, for example, the visual perceptual skills required on the primary levels are not of a very high order of complexity. Reading does, however, impose great demands on the auditory perceptual and auditory sequencing mechanisms as well as the ability to integrate the auditory patterns with visual ones. The child with auditory difficulties may compensate through use of his good visual perceptual abilities *for a short time* but before long partial mastery of the reading skill becomes evident in his failure to be able to sound out unfamiliar words. In learning arithmetic computation the prime requirement seems to be to establish a good visual percept of number groups in relation to another and then to be able to visualize them. The child with good verbal skills and good rote recall will seem to learn the combinations but partial mastery again becomes apparent when they must be used in new and different relationships which have not been drilled as "number facts." This child then cannot visualize the number combinations in relation to other number groups because they were never originally perceived as related quantities.

It seems to us therefore important that the teacher be very familiar with the mental abilities required for mastery of various skills in order to be able to lead the child to employ those abilities rather than permitting him to use substitute ways which will be limiting later on. This may mean that materials or tasks will be designed in such a way that the child is "forced" by the material to take the route required to mastery of the skill and that the teacher must be vigilant and critical of the processes the child uses. Reliance on graded achievement tests is misleading as the grade level score says nothing about the process used by the child in attaining it. For the classroom teacher there is no test to substitute for day-by-day observation and checking not of the end results of the child's practice but of the *manner* in which he obtains his results.

What of the feelings of inadequacy, discouragement and poor self-concept? Very often, as the child sees himself progressing and becoming more like others in school learning at least, he sees himself in a more favorable light. Often substantial personality gains may be made by attacking the learning problems first. The residual problems which still remain may then require the attention of a psychiatrist, or other child mental health worker.

For many a perceptually handicapped child the wall he must scale to be able to enjoy the reaches of knowledge beyond it is a very high one. Bit by bit and inch by inch it can be done, but the work is often arduous and long. An early start in the primary grades is the best insurance that it will be done.[13]

[13] Laura E. Lehtinen, "A Plan for Education," in *Children with Minimal Brain Injury,* Chicago: National Society for Crippled Children and Adults, 1963, pp. 22–24.

Dr. Newell C. Kephart, who is Executive Director of the Achievement Center for Children at Purdue University, gives some cogent guidelines for anyone working with the learning processes of brain-injured children. He explains that it would be helpful for the brain-injured child if we directed attention away from specific performances and toward more generalized behavior. Dr. Kephart explains that effects of brain injury are not so much in interference with specific performances as in development of generalized responses like form perception and concept formation.[14]

The developmental processes are examined by Dr. Kephart, who then explains what those implications are for the classroom:

> In children in whom these earlier stages of development have been inadequate, operation on the higher levels demanded by our educational methods becomes impossible. To continue an attempt to teach such a child at higher stages than his development would warrant sets an impossible task, both for the teacher and for the child. It is necessary in the case of such a child to go back through the stages of development, determine at which stage he has broken down, supply the necessary learnings, insure their integration into generalizations, and reactivate the developmental process. For the brain injured child we will need to make provision in the classroom for teaching the more basic skills at lower levels of development. As these skills can be supplied and as the resulting generalization can be formed, instruction can be advanced to higher levels.[15]

The brain-injured child's inability to generalize plagues him in every phase of his learning process. In order to generalize one has to be able to see the similarities and differences

[14] Newell C. Kephart, *The Brain Injured Child in the Classroom,* Chicago: National Society for Crippled Children and Adults, 1963, p. 1.

[15] *Ibid.,* p. 13.

and the common denominators in certain objects or events. Without the ability to generalize in this fashion, a person cannot organize this knowledge.

Such a child might recognize water coming from the tap of the faucet but not realize that a stream or a swimming pool contain the same properties. A lake, an ocean, and rain may all seem to him totally dissimilar in content. Learning, then, is minute, tedious, step by painful step.

Teachers of brain-damaged children need to walk the delicate balance between using the strong abilities of the child enough to give him confidence and yet calling on the damaged areas in ways that will build their strength. If the child has problems with hearing and speaking, he may be taught through visual perception. The careful analysis of each child and his specific abilities is a necessary and vital component of any program geared to teaching the brain-injured child.

Dr. Charles R. Strother, Director of the Pilot School for the Brain-Injured Child, feels that an educational diagnosis is needed for brain-injured children in order to help in the planning of a program geared toward developing their abilities and compensating for their disabilities. He says, "What is needed as a basis for educational planning is a systematic inventory of the child's level of development in perceptual and motor functions, in communication, in concept formation and in social interaction."[16]

When a child's learning pattern and behavior are such that he requires a special classroom (where they are available), Dr. Strother suggests the following attributes necessary for the teachers:

Teachers who are to be assigned to these special classes should also be carefully selected. Successful teaching with this group

[16] Charles R. Strother, *Discovering . . . Evaluating . . . Programming . . . for the Neurologically Handicapped Child,* Chicago: National Society for Crippled Children and Adults, 1963, pp. 10, 11.

of children is a challenging and demanding job. The most important criterion is the ability of the teacher to establish a satisfying relationship with the children, since her effectiveness in motivating and in reinforcing the child's learning will be largely dependent on this relationship. She must be able to understand and tolerate a great deal of difficult behavior and have some knowledge of the principles involved in modifying this behavior.

She should be skilled in diagnostic teaching, i.e., in the recognition and analysis of the nature of the difficulty which a child is having with a particular task and in the use of ingenuity in devising new materials or different methods to help him overcome or circumvent this difficulty. She should not only be quite familiar with normal developmental sequences in reading, arithmetic, and other academic areas but should also have some knowledge of the basic motor and perceptual processes that are fundamental to reading, communication, and concept formation. She should, of course, be familiar with remedial teaching techniques.

Special physical arrangements for the classroom are desirable. A large open room in which the children can move about freely seems to increase hyperactivity and make control of the group much more difficult. Dividing the room into smaller areas by partitions, with each area used for a different aspect of the program, will not only structure the physical space more satisfactorily but will also help to structure the program for the child. Unnecessary sounds and distracting visual stimuli are disturbing. Carpeted floors, acoustically treated ceilings and walls, opaque windows, storage cabinets where materials not in use can be kept out of sight, and relatively bare walls and blackboards will reduce distractibility. A separate, adjustable desk for each child, facing toward the wall and away from the other children, should be provided. A cubicle where a child can be isolated when he becomes too hyperactive is important—what might be called a "recovery room." Older children will often ask for isolation when things get to be too disturbing for them.

In setting up the school program, the necessity for structure must be kept in mind. The brain-injured child, in particular, may be disturbed by changes in routine and by unexpected situations. A definite sequence of activities should be established, starting when the child comes in the door, goes to hang up his coat and hat, and moves into the area for the first activity of the day. Some definite warning should be provided as a signal to get ready to move into the next activity. The child should be adequately prepared for any change in routine or for a new experience. It should be made clear that routines are not established for authoritarian or disciplinary reasons. They are established to give the child the security of a structured, familiar program and to protect him from unanticipated changes which might impose too great a stress. There must, of course, be reasonable flexibility and the ultimate objective is always to develop the child's ability to adjust to change.[17]

The tedious complexity of the job of teaching children who are brain injured can be seen through the suggestions of the authorities. Both parents and teachers play important parts in the learning process. Dr. Strother suggests the following:

Assuming that a reasonably satisfactory developmental evaluation is available, what is involved in designing an adequate educational program? Ideally, special education for many of these children should begin shortly after birth. If a child's abilities to attend to his environment, to perceive it accurately and to respond to it with an appropriate degree of motor controls are defective, then much of the basic learning that normally takes place in infancy and early childhood will be affected. The child's difficulties in interacting with his environment will, in turn, adversely affect his emotional and social development. There is reason to believe that many of the serious difficulties in child-parent relationships in the families

[17] *Ibid.*, pp. 12, 13.

of these children are the product not of any primary psycho-pathology in the parent but of the parents' inability to under-stand and respond effectively to the child's basic difficulties. If supervision and instruction could be provided from the beginning, many of the problems that are seen at the time the child enters school might never have developed. It must be admitted that little is yet known about techniques for the management and training of the very young brain-injured child but an increasing amount of material addressed to parents is appearing and research on the early stages of development is in process. Parent education must also be an important part of any school program lest the benefits derived from the school training be counteracted by disturbing factors in the home.

In the school, brain-injured children and children exhibit-ing similar problems of behavior and learning will frequently require special classes. They are often too disturbing an influence in classes for slow learners or for the mentally re-tarded and their special needs can seldom be met in classes for the emotionally disturbed. The selection of children for these special classes should be determined by the child's needs rather than by the establishment of a definitive diagnosis of brain injury. If the child exhibits, to a significant degree, the syndrome which has been described and if his progress in a regular class or in classes designed for other types of children is not satisfactory, then he should be placed in a class with children who present problems similar to his. The teacher should have a voice in the decision on admission or retention of each child, since group cohesiveness and constructive peer relationships are essential if the children are to make signifi-cant progress.[18]

An apocryphal story is told that a physician interviewed a mother and her hyperactive, slow-learning, distractible child in his clinic. The mother's face showed the signs of the long struggle between herself and her son. She recounted the

18 *Ibid.,* pp. 11, 12.

many false starts—the numerous pediatricians, child guidance clinic personnel, school counselors, and well-meaning friends who had advised her about her Albert, to no avail.

The physician administered the Wechsler Intelligence Scale for Children and the Bender Visual Motor Gestalt. The large discrepancy between Verbal and Performance IQ scores on the WISC and the type of drawings on the Gestalt began to give some clues. Further studies were made, including developmental history of Albert, a school history, reading competency tests, and an electroencephalogram. As in the case of Joel, Albert was found to have some "short circuits," and the doctor put him on medication and also prescribed a carefully designed tutorial program.

When the mother returned with Albert six months later, the physician asked about Albert's progress.

"Oh, doctor, it's wonderful," the mother said. "He takes his medicine regularly. He was able to bring his math grade up from an 'F' to a 'C—.' He is going to pass math." The mother paused and cleared her throat. "Doctor," she said, "may I ask you one more favor?"

"Of course," replied the physician.

"Could you give Albert a pill for English?"

Unfortunately, no magic pill exists . . . only the patient, loving, knowledgeable care of parents and educators working together can bring about that "magic" ability for the child with learning difficulties.

CHAPTER IV

PLACES AND PERSONS—SOURCES OF HELP
"God Tempers the Wind"

WHAT CAN BE DONE for the child with learning disabilities? How can parents know where to take him and how to help him? Where do they go for diagnosis, for treatment, for rehabilitation? The variety of methods, schools of thought, and basic principles expressed concerning the child with learning difficulties may serve to confuse the parent and lead him either into apathetic helplessness or frantic movement. The parent may react in the same way that the brain-injured child does to stimuli—by attending to many of them in quick sequence.

What can any parent do when he begins to suspect that his child may have some learning disability, either minor or severe? To whom can he turn, and how can he know that the opinion he has received is valid?

In this chapter we shall see how one family was able to find help. After that, we shall visit four facilities which treat youngsters who have learning problems. Two of them, the Houston Speech and Hearing Center and the Institute for Language Disorders, are nonresidential. Two others, the Pathway School and the Menninger Foundation provide residential care.

In order to see what happened to one little boy, let us go into the Barclay home and be invisible guests.

It is a lovely home. The morning sun filtered through the nylon curtains gives a dappled effect to the beige carpet. Meg Barclay rushes from kitchen wing to bedroom wing, hurrying children, a mother hen clucking her chicks out of the house. She is pretty in a distracted sort of way. Her honey-colored hair is tied back with one of the girls' orange pieces of yarn, and her gold print housedress gives a gayer appearance than her face, which is slightly drawn and pensive. Herbert comes in hurriedly, briefcase in hand. He pats Meg on the shoulder, rushes out the door. The car starts, and he backs out of the driveway and disappears around the corner. The dog whines. Meg lets him out the kitchen door while calling, "Fay, hurry. Your car pool will be here in three minutes. Henrietta, do you remember the dentist appointment after school? I'll pick you up if you call me when you're through."

A sound of crashing glass shatters Meg's words. She shudders and then goes into one of the bedrooms. The girls appear briefly, as on a stage set. A car honks, and they are gone, leaving behind the whisper of cologne and hair spray.

Meg, meanwhile, picks up the pieces of a light bulb, which a few minutes before was part of the lamp on Bill's dresser. Bill watches the pickup process for a minute, then busies himself with dumping a box of crayons on the floor and methodically breaking them. Bill does this without anger, simply as another child might put together a puzzle.

Meg looks up and quietly takes inventory of the room and of this son who baffles and disturbs her.

He is small for his almost-six years, and that is good. Otherwise how could one explain the nursery school personnel who diagnosed him "immature" or the kindergarten teacher who called him too disruptive to stay in school? Now that this year is an optional one so far as his entrance into school is concerned, Meg knows that this must be the time of reckoning.

She sits back in the corner of the room and reflects about Bill, who seems to turn into nothing the competencies she thought were hers as a mother. Of course there are problems with Henrietta and Fay. Did any girl reach adolescence without rebellion and anger and a conflict of interests? But the girls' problems are some she can understand. She shares them with her friends, whose children act the same way.

But no one else has a child like Bill. No other infant among the families of her contemporaries was so slow to sit up and to crawl. None of them failed to speak or to respond to game playing. Not one has stayed at home for all of the preschool years. Meg draws a hand across her forehead and smiles bitterly. She used to tell a joke about a little girl in nursery school who failed sandpiling. The joke has turned sour, and Meg's smile dissolves into the lines around her mouth.

Bill, who has broken all of the crayons, and has started jumping up and down on his bed, suddenly stops and begins to sob, great wracking sobs of anguish. Meg springs to her feet and starts for her son. Then she pauses, for she knows from many experiences that this kind of crying cannot be soothed by the gentle touch of a mother's hand nor the caressing words she might offer. It is as if Bill is in another room or another world or another bit of space. His weeping is for something she cannot fathom. Meg stands in the middle of the disordered room and stares at the blond-haired youngster who is her son and who is now weeping. She can neither understand nor comfort him.

Meg glances at her watch, goes out of Bill's room, and rushes around straightening the house. She and Bill are to see the new pediatrician in town, Dr. Howard, at ten o'clock. Will it be the same old routine Meg wonders. A physical appraisal. A "Your son is a healthy specimen. He'll be playing football on Central's team one of these days. Don't worry about his slowness in talking or his acting out. He'll outgrow them."

He'll outgrow them. How many times has she heard those words? A hundred? A thousand? Kindly friends have put it thus, "Meg, you're just expecting Bill to act like the girls. Boys are different, you know." Meg finishes making up the girls' beds, rushes into her room to dress. All the while she reflects that there is a difference in Bill which has nothing to do with boys and girls. She could understand a slower growth pattern, delayed speech, or lack of good coordination. But Bill has been too erratic in behavior, too competent in some areas and far too slow in others, too unaware of family action, too much apart to be simply a slow runner on a fast team. From early babyhood on he has been unlike other babies she has observed, and now the difference can be seen in his destructive, hyperactive, acting-out behavior.

Meg sinks down on the side of her bed. It is almost more than she can endure. Every morning she wonders if she will be able to make it through the day. Her nerves are taut as violin strings; she is ten pounds thinner than at this time last year; threads of gray are appearing in her blonde hair. Meg sighs and begins to dress . . .

Dr. Howard's office is nearly empty. For this Meg is thankful. Bill is running in fast circles around the room, and Meg's head is spinning at the same rate. The nurse motions her and Bill into Dr. Howard's office. Meg feels a sense of instant relief as Dr. Howard begins his methodical and thorough examination. Finally Bill is taken away by the nurse, and Dr. Howard gives Meg his full attention.

He asks innumerable questions. Did she take many drugs during delivery? Did Bill breathe immediately after birth? What kinds of illnesses did Bill have as an infant and tiny child? Were there prolonged high temperatures? What were Bill's sleep patterns? How did he suck as an infant? What are his activities now? Is he destructive? How does he act toward younger children and animals?

Meg answers carefully, aware that this man is not about

to brush away her anxieties nor to tell her that Bill will out-grow his present behavior. Dr. Howard instead comes from behind his desk, takes a chair near Meg, and listens as she talks about all of her anxieties about Bill, about his uneven kind of development, his skills at certain tasks and his inability at others; about his behavior, uncontrollable and unpredictable.

When she has finished, Dr. Howard recommends a complete workup by a neurologist and psychologist. "Bill may be brain-injured," he says, "but I want a thorough and complete battery of tests to help me in prescribing a method of treatment for Bill. . . ."

Meg leaves Dr. Howard's office holding close to her the precious jewel of hope. Although a diagnosis of brain-injury is not joy-producing, it does at least put a name to all of the vague fears, the serious worries, and the terrifying phantoms. If Bill acts as he does because he is injured, Meg can work with the doctors and the educators to find out how to help him. Dr. Howard has said there is medication for the hyperactivity and educational methods for learning.

Meg gulps her first swallow of hope, water to her parched throat. Dr. Howard has discussed with her the educational system in Central and has already pointed out that if Bill's diagnosis comes out as he thinks it will, there may be some problems in trying to find classrooms into which Bill can fit.

"Because our recognition of brain-injury and its educational problems is so new, many school and community people have failed to understand the need which these children have for specialized classes," Dr. Howard told Meg. "The room for handicapped children *per se* will not do for Bill nor for youngsters like him," the physician added. "Bill's hyperactivity, his quick and violent response to stimuli, and his tantrums will keep him from being welcomed in such classes."

Still Dr. Howard offered a possible solution. "With women like you who are stable and intelligent, we often recommend as a temporary solution that the mother serve as a teacher, with a great deal of help from teachers in the regular school system. If you are taught the techniques of keeping Bill quiet and attentive, you can help him a great deal. We have recently acquired in Central's school system a Miss Henderson, who is well trained in special education and who has worked in the past with many brain-injured children. We can ask her to supervise you along the way."

Meg protested. "If Miss Henderson is so good and so well-trained, why isn't there simply a class for brain-injured children with Miss Henderson teaching it?"

"It's not quite that simple," Dr. Howard responded. "In the first place, Miss Henderson was employed to supervise all of the special education programs in our entire school system. In the second place, Bill's great distractibility and activity demonstrate that he may be better off in an extremely quiet school room where there is no added stimulus from outside or from other children."

Meg remembers staring at the desk top. She was afraid to look at Dr. Howard. Then she said quietly, "Dr. Howard, I would do anything I could for any of my children. You must know that. But I cannot see giving up the next twelve years to being a schoolteacher and neglecting all of the other interests I have for the girls, for Herbert, or myself."

Dr. Howard patted her shoulder. "We are not talking about twelve years, or ten, or six. We have found, increasingly, that a brain-injured child, after one or two or three years of special training, may then be able to join in group activities with others in his school and then may be able to go into special or regular classes. If we find that that is not true with Bill, we shall look for a residential school where he can be taught and trained simultaneously."

When she had returned home, Meg sat down in the den and thought through all that Dr. Howard had told her. She could hardly wait until Herbert came home. Dr. Howard wanted an appointment with Herbert in order to talk of Herbert's own responsibility and need to devote more time to his family, especially Bill and Meg. "Grown men can hide behind their work when they are afraid to face a problem at home." Those were Dr. Howard's words.

There was a long road ahead. Meg knew it. But now she had a road map, a sense of direction, a knowledge that there was a clearing somewhere. Already she sensed a new strength within her, and a renewed recognition of what life must be like for Bill. She began to feel a bit of his anguish, a small bird beating against a giant pane of glass. Instead of anger at his destructiveness, she empathized with his inner panic. For the first time in many years she remembered a ride at the carnival which came into town one weekend when she was a child. She had insisted on riding in the swinging chairs, which rushed ahead and bumped into others, threw her backward and forward and far around. She had grown so terrified that she could not even cry out. And when the ride had stopped, she did not know where she was, how to get out of the seat, nor where to go. Her father had stepped forward, unbuckled her, held her in his strong arms, and her panic had subsided.

Surely they could do as much for Bill.

† † †

The Barclays were able to find some satisfactory solutions to their difficulties. However, if Meg Barclay had lived in some other community, a tiny rural one without specialized services of a pediatrician or a larger town where there was no counterpart for Dr. Howard, where could she have turned? Even another pediatrician as good as Dr. Howard might not have been greatly helpful had Bill had only functional or psychological symptoms rather than some physical manifestations.

How does a parent know when he is indulging in "the search," the frantic running from physician to physician to try to find an acceptable answer to a problem? How can he know what is cautious seeking of answers and what is blind running from a problem?

Perhaps no question has been more difficult for parents of a deviant child to answer. Some suggestions made by a pediatrician may serve as guidelines.

First of all, parents can begin selection by asking among their neighbors, other doctors, and the physician himself about whether or not he is interested in the child who may be handicapped. The parent should feel free to make inquiries of him concerning his background and his interests.

Or the parents can seek out a university-oriented hospital clinic. Most communities are within easy traveling distance of a university, and parents can make inquiries by writing directly to the university information service or to a child development center or children's outpatient clinic on campus.

Still another route is through the mental health/mental retardation community centers, which are now operating in many local communities and in various regions. State offices of mental health and mental retardation can give information about location.

A fourth possibility is to check with the state health department, which increasingly keeps lists of clinics and centers in a state. A community evaluation center in the nearest large city can also serve as a source of information about services.

The parent needs to feel free to ask questions. An understanding schoolteacher or principal may give some suggestions about sensitive physicians. The parent may well ask his pediatrician if he feels that referral to some other source, such as a neurologist or clinic, is in order. Where speech centers exist, they can often serve as auxiliary evaluation sources for the child. Some medical schools provide free treatment as learning experiences for interns. In a number of rural areas traveling teams exist to bring coordinated services to isolated communities.

Wherever there is a child guidance center, a mental health clinic, or a mental retardation center, the parent may go for advice and assistance.

In summary, the child with real problems will not "outgrow" them without professional and careful help. Most parents would prefer to spend time and money learning through diagnostic tests that their child is normal than to lose precious weeks and months waiting for a youngster to "outgrow" a problem which must be dealt with eventually.

Meg Barclay was fortunate to find a Dr. Howard close by. However, every parent can locate well-trained teams to evaluate his child if he is willing to check the nearby sources.

When a scientific evaluation has been made, parents have taken the first large step toward understanding what it is that hurts their child and what they can do to help assuage the ache.

Four Facilities

After the first giant step has been taken, parents still need to determine what is best specifically for their child at that time. Where local school systems and other resources are not sufficient or where the disability of the child or the disruption of the family is so great that the youngster cannot be helped sufficiently, auxiliary resources must be found.

Four facilities will be visited on these pages. They are not representative of the scope of treatment programs. Rather, they have been chosen more for their nonspecificity than for any single mode of treatment. The first two will be the non-residential centers; the second two the ones providing total care.

First of all, let us go to Houston, Texas, and see a program geared toward helping people gain competence in communication.

HOUSTON SPEECH AND HEARING CENTER

At the Houston Speech and Hearing Center, vivacious Dr. Tina Bangs says, "Teach children, not materials." And she believes in teaching them young. Petite two-year-olds attend class daily. Infants only a few days old are tested for hearing loss.

"The crucial years from birth to four need to be utilized," Dr. Bangs believes. "During this time a child's infinite number of neurological networks have not been subjected to the variety of stimuli and interference found in the older child's brain."

Preschoolers are special members of the Houston Speech and Hearing Center program, although older children and survivors of strokes are also treated there. The Center, which is housed on the Texas Medical Center campus, began in a limited way in 1952 as a diagnostic center. Now, in an effort to habilitate and rehabilitate patients, about 4,000 classroom sessions a year are held. A large research complex is part of the Center, and training teachers is a part of the Center's program.

The husband-and-wife team of Drs. Jack and Tina Bangs has, for 15 years, been single-mindedly working in the area of communication. Dr. Jack, who serves as director of the Center, concerns himself with administration and research. Dr. Tina holds responsibility for much of the programming.

Red-haired Tina Bangs exudes enthusiasm and optimism. In her sunny office, which is filled with color, she talks of the need for early identification and assessment of a child's assets and deficits which may be related to future academic achievement. "We should teach skills early, before they are needed," she believes.

"The time to make an appointment for language assessment is when the parent, physician, or a relative or friend first suspects that the child has a problem," she says. Her aim is to help the child develop skills early and satisfactorily and to shunt the emotional problems which often accompany learning disabilities.

All kinds of communication problems are considered at the Center. An ongoing program with the parents is instituted and continued, and the parents become part of every phase of the child's procedures. Enforcement of discipline is emphasized for the parents who may tend to overprotect a child with difficulties. Recognizing that hyperactive children who are undisciplined become real school problems, the staff at the Center works intensively on achieving suitable social behavior.

The Center staff recognizes that for some children reading problems are a unique combination of maladies. "A few short years ago virtually nothing was known about this subject. Now we know that some can recall what they just *read,* and others cannot. We also know that some can recall what they just *heard,* and others cannot."[1] In a classroom, the staff observes, a child's brain is not waiting in a vacuum. The "normal" child can make a quick shift when the teacher speaks. But the child with a disordered brain mechanism cannot do so. He has internal noise which is affecting his reception of the message. "We have no remedy for 'discrimination loss' of hearing—the affliction in which normal sound becomes distorted to the listener, something like garbled radio reception in a storm."[2]

[1] *These Are Exceptional Children.* Houston: Houston Speech and Hearing Center, Annual Report, 1964.
[2] *Ibid.*

Although they do not have the remedy for such distorted listening, the Center staff has developed techniques for helping such children to achieve increasing competence in listening, looking, and learning. The basic task is in finding the level upon which the youngster is functioning in specific modalities of language and learning.

Let us visit one classroom where children aged from two and a half to four are in attendance. The tots meet in groups because life itself is organized in that way, and much learning must take place in just that fashion.

Four little persons are seated at pint-sized desks. There is Julie, yellow-haired and chubby. And Dave, whose feet and hands are in constant motion. Michael's eyes are everywhere, out the window, to the right, to the left, at his feet, up to the ceiling. Ellie's liquid brown eyes stay on the teacher, but her brown legs and arms keep moving.

To the casual observer they look like a quartet of youngsters in any play preschool session. But in this classroom everything is done with a purpose and for its strengthening qualities. The teacher sits in front of the children and sees that they attend her face, and especially her lips, as she speaks. The chief difference noticeable between this group and the usual preschoolers is that these children stay in their seats. The first lesson which they are taught is to attend to the teacher and to control their movements. The philosophy behind this action is that children need education in classroom learning. These particular children, because of their problems, will have a harder time than most in any learning situation. If, in addition to their learning problems, they have behavioral difficulties, they will not be able to progress in school. Therefore, from the early age of two, they are put into classes and are taught to stay still for the period of the session. There is no hopping up or changing seats or hitting one another. The first phrase the children learn is "Sit down," said calmly but firmly. By the time they get to school, they have acquired good work habits.

Constant stimulation is given to these children. Their own output of language may come much later. Today the teacher has a box of sand and two shovels. A game for fun? No, indeed. Most of the children live near the seashore and will be exposed to the sand and the water. The teacher is building on actual experiences of the child to help him learn.

The teacher invites Ellie to the front of the room and holds her hand in the sand. Lifting it, she says clearly, "Brush it off." "Brush it off." No more than four words are used at a time with the children.

Michael shuffles forward next. The teacher takes his hand and digs deeply into the sandbox. Michael brings out a rubber doll. "It's a doll," says the teacher. "It's a doll."

Now, in subtle manner, concepts of large and small are given. Julie stands before the teacher, who says, "Take the big shovel." Julie reaches for the smaller one. "Take the big one," the teacher says, and then fills the bucket from the large shovel and from the small one. A small car makes tracks in the sand; the group learns the difference between car tracks and baby tracks and dog tracks. The children acquire kinesthetic sense of knowing how things feel, a prelude to developing writing skills. Big and little, likes and opposites—these come to them in numerous ways. They begin to store ideas and to know that what is said and what is felt mean something.

When attention begins to wander, another activity is begun, but the learning goal is always paramount. "The handicap must not rule out the learning ability," say members of the staff. The appeal is made to the areas of wellness in these children.

Conferences are held with the parents two days a week,

and once a week there is a group conference where parents can share their anxieties and their observations. Some questions may come from the tired mother in a cotton skirt and blouse whose child attends the classes free and who herself is given bus fare to bring her to the Center. Other comments may be made by women whose incomes and education surpass the dreams of the other mother. Yet the parents work in common concern for their children and are taught together how to make each hour of every day meaningful in their relationships with their youngsters.

The staff feels that a residential school is desirable under three conditions: (1) when no acceptable day schools are available, (2) when parents' travel programs are such that children have to keep changing schools, or (3) when parents do not want to reinforce what is learned at school.

INSTITUTE FOR LANGUAGE DISORDERS

A comprehensive center for treatment and diagnosis of children with problems in learning is the Institute for Language Disorders in Evanston, Illinois. There Dr. Helmer R. Myklebust, well known for his work with such children, continues the long and tedious search for reasons behind learning disabilities and ways of reaching those youngsters. Dr. Myklebust's interest was spurred when, as a teacher of the deaf, he saw many children whose hearing was not impaired but who could not understand what was said to them. He also knew that many youngsters with perfect vision were unable to read. Intrigued, he went into clinical psychology and education and continued his search into ways in which language develops. Now he is professor of language pathology and psychology and director of the Institute for Language Disorders. His right hand aide is attractive and energetic Doris Johnson, who supervises the therapy for the Institute.

Although the wet breath of Lake Michigan touches the

building where the Institute is, the lake cannot be seen from the testing and therapy rooms which have small, high windows. The distractible and hyperactive children must not be distracted from the problem at hand, that of learning language. Both Dr. Myklebust and Miss Johnson have infinite, delicate, patient ability at working with the young people, whether it be in diagnosis or in therapy. Many families reach the Institute after having run the gamut of recommended services. They are already discouraged, tired, and out of hope. However, under the patient testing of Dr. Myklebust, the youngsters are able to demonstrate those skills they have and to show where some of the gaps in their abilities lie. During the procedure, the process is monitored behind a one-way window in order that every clue concerning the child will be picked up and noted. A nine-page form stating everything from physical appearance to behavior is completed.

Immediately following a diagnostic session, Dr. Myklebust goes to the other side of the one-way window and holds a conference with the staff members who have been watching him. These may be teachers or doctoral candidates or psychologists. Much of the Institute time is devoted to training graduate students. In Illinois, legislation specifies certain requirements for the teacher of children with learning disabilities.

Many combinations of programs are held at the Institute. There are half-day clinics for preschoolers. Referrals come from all states in the Union and from numerous foreign countries. About 75 children are in therapy at any one time.

Trim Dr. Myklebust takes pride in the physical setup of his Institute, but his greatest pride comes when a youngster like Pete, who was locked into a nonverbal world and whose behavior was such that no school could contain him, came to the Institute and finally learned the order of the universe and the means of making sense of printed words.

Numerous studies are going on at the Institute. One of

128   *Your Nonlearning Child*

them involves waking brain studies; others are highly specialized electroencephalograms. Some projects concern teaching
methods; others, diagnosis. One involves a population of third-
and fourth-graders, a total of 800 children, in order to evaluate ways in which normal and damaged children learn and
understand what is spoken to them.

Dr. Myklebust thinks we should use all methods to try to
help children with learning disorders, some of whom are considered retarded because of their deficits. "An amazing example," says Dr. Myklebust, "is that of one young boy who
turned out to have an IQ of 200. Imagine losing such a person! And he was in process of being shunted away when he
was brought to us."

Doris Johnson echoes Dr. Myklebust's enthusiasm concerning helping these children with learning disorders. No clue
is too small for her to follow. She keeps a file cabinet of case
materials and will show with pleasure the garbled handwriting
of a young man who was able to mobilize his abilities and to
obtain a graduate degree by using a tape recorder. Or she may
talk gently of the little boy to whom language became all
garbled, like a radio with too much static.

If you see her on the other side of the one-way glass as she
works with a little straw-haired youngster we shall call Kevin,
you will see what seems like a relaxed young woman talking
with a little boy across the table. So skillful is she and so easy
in manner that Kevin himself is able to be at ease. Miss Johnson has a dozen different ways of trying to teach a child the
ability to symbolize or to generalize. With Kevin, for example,
she takes out a picture book and points to an illustration of a
dog. She says "dog," and takes Kevin's fingers to her lips in
order that he can feel the movement of her mouth as she says
the word. She brings out a toy dog and has him hold it. She
sings a song about a dog and asks him to draw a picture of a

dog. Each of these seemingly simple tasks is a desperate endeavor to help Kevin's mind make the jump between a word and an object. It is this great disability in putting information into a whole which makes learning disabilities like these so painful for many children. Everything is disconnected in their minds, and they are unable to anticipate or to recall objects or the meaning of them in their lives. Boys like Kevin cannot orient themselves in time or space. It takes a teacher with multiple skills and infinite patience to search for and find the combination which can open the mind of such a child.

When a child is taken into the Institute program, careful counseling is given the parents in order that they can help him at every step of the way. The home environment can make a colossal difference, and as parents begin to learn what is wrong with their child and how he perceives the world, they are able to alter both their home setting and their behavior toward him in a way which will help him. They cut off television, put the simplest of table tools before him at mealtime, curtail parties and shopping trips. They see that the child has a schedule which, as nearly as possible, is unvaried day after day after day. In this way the youngster is able to get some idea of an ordered universe at home at the same time that he is learning the skills of communication at the Institute itself.

Sandy might serve as an example.[3] When he came to Dr. Myklebust, he was eight years and four months old and had an IQ of at least 150. He showed much more visual ability than auditory, and he could not "sound out" the simplest words. He could not spell nor write, nor could he give the days of the week or the months of the year in sequence. Sandy had much trouble with any task requiring auditory abilities, such as

[3] Helmer R. Myklebust, "Dyslexia in Children," in *Exceptional Children,* Washington, D.C.: Council for Exceptional Children, Vol. 29, No. 1, September 1962, pp. 21, 22.

learning the sounds that letters make. Although he continued
to have much trouble with spelling, at the termination of his
training, Sandy was advanced three years in reading. When his
remedial work was over, Sandy was put into a class for the
gifted.

Although the staff working with Dr. Myklebust at the
Institute would be the first to state how many unknowns exist
in any programs for language-disordered children, they are
excited about the possibilities for discovery. And they rejoice
when boys like Sandy and Kevin are able to find their way,
with help, through the jungle of their gigantic disabilities and
into a bright land where there is order and sameness and a
world which is predictable.

† † †

Now let us look at two other centers which are geared
toward giving 24-hour-a-day service. When the "brokenness"
of Bill or Julie or Michael is such that it cannot be mended at
home, where do you turn?

One place may be the Pathway School at Norristown,
Pennsylvania, a school designed for the brain-injured child.

The Pathway School

The very setting of the Pathway School bespeaks both strength
and beauty. The rolling hills near the Schuylkill River, the tall
trees around the buildings, and the green lawns represent
stability and shelter of nature. The administration building
signifies its ancient ancestry. Like a Dutch patriarch, it looks
over the modern one-story structures designed especially for
Pathway's teaching methods and small classes. A gymnasium-
auditorium and residential cottages round out the complex of
buildings for the school.

Heading the program is Pathway's founder and president,

Dr. Sheldon Rappaport, who has maintained a continuing interest in aphasic and brain-damaged children for a number of years. The energy which Dr. Rappaport exudes spills over onto his staff, all of whom seem to carry an air of quiet urgency about the work which they are doing. A young man, Dr. Rappaport smiles easily, but his eyes, when he talks about his work with the children, are like blue flames. He cares greatly what happens to the young people in his charge. Or, as he puts it, ". . . we at Pathway are only *beginning* to understand enough about the *problems* to attempt solutions sufficiently knowledgeable to be assured some modicum of success."[4]

He seems to be everywhere—meeting with staff, with children, with parents, with board members. The program at Pathway itself is a continuous pattern of relationships between the children and the staff and the staff members themselves.

Day begins with a rush at Pathway. By 8:30 in the morning staff members have assembled in the gymnasium. Many of them come much earlier. Those who have been on night duty seem a bit red-rimmed around the eyes. The daytime workers shuck their raincoats or other wraps, lay them on some of the tables in the gymnasium. All of them wander to the large coffee urn, help themselves, and then break into small groups for conversations about special children or special problems.

These morning conferences are scheduled. But all during the day other conferences are held when a crisis occurs or an incipient problem needs solving. Difficulties are handled as they happen.

Let's look at one typical morning.

[4] Sheldon Rappaport, "Relationship Structure," in *Childhood Aphasia and Brain Damage,* Vol. III, Narberth, Pennsylvania: Livingston Publishing Company, 1966, p. 1.

At one corner of the gymnasium a small group assembles around a table. There are several visitors from other centers, two consultants to the school, Dr. Rappaport, and a team of specialists, including the child development workers, the teachers, the skill builder, and the physical therapist.

Under discussion is Michael. During the evening he snatched Fred's school workbook and tore it into six pieces. He hid Jimmy's shoes, threw food at the supper table. In school he had a tantrum.

The young housemother, her eyes intent on the group, picks at her pink sweater as she relates Michael's afterschool behavior. Each contributor to the story concerns himself, not only with what Mike did, but with what might have happened inside of Mike to make him need to thrash about as he did.

The group pieces together one item and another into the complicated puzzle which is Mike—red-haired Mike, who looks as if he should be playing peewee football instead of struggling to master some of the basic skills of reading and motor coordination.

Was Mike's medication changed in any way? Were there evidences the day before that trouble might be spiraling inside of him? What about his relationships with other children? Was there some threatening new school problem which might have upset him? These questions are asked and answers given by each person who saw Mike or worked with him over a period of several days. Together, patiently, piece by piece, the group works on, trying to see the whys of Mike's behavior and attempting to find ways of dealing with it constructively.

The earnest teacher, too young to have a son the age of Mike, leans over the table and speaks with a kind of parental concern. The special teacher, the skill area specialist, traces Mike's activities of the afternoon before. Her voice softens as she repeats a moment when Mike reached for her hand and held it as he worked.

Continuous relationships may well be the two words which characterize the Pathway School. Young people who have been out of control come to the Pathway School, where they find a constant environment. These children, Dr. Rappaport says, have insufficient impulse control or regulation, inadequate integrative functions, and defective self-concept. For them, the environment is structured in such a way as to help the child organize the stimuli in it meaningfully. By the time they reach the Pathway School most of these children have known years of failure and conflict.

When damage comes to the central nervous system, the child's ego development suffers. Then, as we have seen earlier, a cyclical pattern of mother-child negative responses begins and spirals. The child who cannot suck and who falls asleep during nursing gives little satisfaction to the mother. She then responds to this child in a different way from her responses to other and normal children, either by rejecting or by overprotecting the child, and this altered maternal response combines with his already defective ego to interfere with his development and his growth and his sense of competence. Again, as was pointed out, when some of these children finally develop the ability to move on their own, they race through the day as if they cannot move fast enough or far enough. They are the children who swing from the drapes in the living room, turn over the chairs in the dining room, smash windows in the house, break chairs, all in the space of an hour.

They are proud of their ability to act; their mothers are driven to distraction by their destructiveness and lack of control.

And then they come, belatedly, to the Pathway School.

Not all of these children, however, are hyperactive. According to Dr. Rappaport, almost as large a number of these children are "passive resisters." "These are the youngsters," says Dr. Rappaport,

> who control parents and the rest of the environment by daring them to make him do what is requested. One child may sit down in the middle of the street at the busiest intersection of any city and then blame the parent who moved him for causing all of the resultant problems. He behaves similarly to the teacher who tries to introduce learning tasks which he regards as fraught with frustration or failure. This child requires as much special handling and understanding as does the acting-out hyperactive child.
>
> In general the approach to him is the same as to the acting-out youngster, with the understanding that the teacher needs to make contact with him and to reassure him that he need not be afraid of the new situation because it is really no more difficult for him than that which he has already achieved in other areas. As his fear of various situations diminishes, he has less need to control them by his passive resisting.[5]

At the school the children have a reverse kind of decompression chamber. Each person relating to the child is asked to begin with him at the level at which he is functioning. Each person communicates in some way to this child that he understands the child's struggles. In addition, he lets the child know that he neither fears nor rejects him; he demonstrates to the youngster that certain defensive patterns of behavior will need to be given up—but not until the child has the strength to replace them with others. The staff members are told that they must provide the total life structure for the young people as long as they need it. "And it is your responsibility to realize

[5] Letter from Dr. Rappaport, 1967.

that the core of that total-life-structure is your ability to relate with him in a fashion which says, 'I am here to *help* you, not to hurt you or to have a contest of wills with you; to help you recognize your problems and limitations and suffering so that you can overcome them and begin to use effectively and joyously the assets I know you have.' "[6]

Many persons relate to the children at the Pathway School. They have various competencies and varied training, but they work by the philosophy expressed by Dr. Rappaport.

The school buildings are attractive, much like other small schools, yet different. They are quiet. Very quiet. Classrooms are carpeted, and the usual blackboard, bulletin board, garish pictures, and cutouts are absent. All of the classrooms are built around a center well. Each room holds from six to eight children, and each child works within his own cubicle.

Here Mary bends over a wide-lined tablet and laboriously copies an "A" from a cutout on the desk before her. David awkwardly works the abacus as he tries to solve an arithmetic problem in his workbook. Rangy Dick stares into space, then is distracted by the visitors, suddenly rushes to the wall to sharpen his pencil. Frank squints as he copies a line from a book. His pencil breaks, and before he can react to its brokenness, his teacher stands beside him with another pencil in her hand. A second teacher walks quietly from child to child, always touching the youngster on the shoulder or on the arm, always conveying in silent language, "I am here with you. I am here to help you and to give you strength."

Under the umbrella of such quiet competence many children are able to mobilize their inner ability and to build constructively. However, the tightrope they walk is very thin and very high, and they may slip at any instant. For instance, Frank falls to the floor in a catastrophic collapse. This is not

[6] Rappaport, *op. cit.,* p. 8.

the tantrum of an angry child nor the attention-getting of a spoiled one. It is the falling apart of a framework which has been built slowly, gently, strongly, like so many matchsticks in a child's fortress. Without comment the teacher bends over Frank, helps him up, and without emotion aids him in picking up one by one the mythical matchsticks to rebuild the framework of his being.

Both during and after the regular school hours skill area specialists work with the children. Usually this aid is given in conjunction with the regular class program, but sometimes it is rendered on an individual basis, in addition to the classroom work. The specialists work individually with the young people to help them develop abilities in their areas of greatest weaknesses. They aid them with the homework and with their egos. Children from both the upper and lower schools have special instruction, though the upper school is less stimulus-controlled than the lower one is.

There are some day students. They come to the school by bus and train. At the beginning of the year a staff member may travel with them to help set the patterns and expectations for the children. However, reliance is placed mostly on older children, who are called "safeties," to provide the external source of support for those who might lose control. The term "older children" is used to refer to those who have been in the program long enough to be able to handle effectively both their own impulses and their relationships with others.

Once in the school setting, the children participate in all of the same activities as do the resident students, who stay from one to four years, with an average stay of three years.

The formal school day is only a small piece of the therapeutic cloth spread around the child at Pathway. Mealtimes in the cottages are homelike but with the addition of constant observers who note a child's restlessness or his withdrawal, his mood changes, and his actions toward others. The house parents, young and pleasant, give the same assurance of strength and constancy which characterizes the remainder of the Pathway staff.

The organization of cottage life in large measure replicates family life. Two children live in each room, and a large living room gives space for play activity. The difference lies, once again, on the absence of numerous stimuli. There is a sparsity of pictures and knickknacks and garish colors. Rather, the large windows opening onto the rolling countryside and the subdued carpeting of the rooms give an atmosphere of peace and of continuity. The children's rooms are attractive though spartan. There are the young evidences of individuality—family pictures, a small radio, a book or two—but here again stimuli are at a minimum. Everywhere he turns, the brain-injured child can achieve a feeling of competent strength and security.

The child development workers take over the physical activity program when the school day ends. Their job is to help the child in all after-school and in weekend activities. Through the residential coordinator, the after-school program for the children is dovetailed with the educational program to enhance the child's development of preacademic and academic abilities, as well as other ego skills.

The gymnasium hums with action. Swimming hours are fun—but they are also times for learning. In the water, under instruction, a child achieves motor skills and ability to develop laterality. The basketball hoop is for skill training in ball placement—and also in developing orientation of the child in space and in helping him to use his body in a strengthening manner. Walking foot over foot on a plank of wood is a youngster's delight—and also a means of helping the brain-damaged child to achieve balance and visual perception. Other equipment is utilized for motor and perceptual skill-building exercises.

Parents are very much a part of the Pathway program. Regularly scheduled meetings are held, permitting the parents to share their anxieties and to discuss the problems which they meet daily when the brain-damaged child is in the home. Problems are freely brought into the open, and the Pathway staff members discuss with parents how similar problems are dealt with in the school. This combining of resources permits a doubling of efforts between parents and staff to help the child develop. Parents of day students can attend such conferences frequently; fathers and mothers of the residential students have visitations and conferences prior to vacation periods.

Preschoolers are also part of the Pathway program. Here the work with parents is intensified in order that they can carry out at home a program which may help to prevent the syndrome of learning and behavioral difficulties which occurs when brain damage is not diagnosed at an early age.

The therapy does not need to end when the child leaves school. Contact is made by the Pathway staff with the teachers in the school to which the child will go. Information is given, and the Pathway members stand ready to serve as consultants at any time. The children themselves may return for counseling, and so may their parents.

After children graduate from Pathway, if they need continuing psychotherapy or academic help, these are provided by the staff. However, most graduates do not need such auxiliary aid. After a mean stay at Pathway of about three years, about 80 per cent of the children are returning to regular classes one year behind grade level.

A recent graduate, a young man, indicated that the one provision which the Pathway School had not made was the hiring of a teacher who himself was brain-injured. Therefore, said the graduate, he intends to go to college and to return to a teaching job at Pathway.

Perhaps the philosophy of the Pathway School was best summed up by its president, Dr. Sheldon Rappaport, who has stated that once the child has been identified as brain-damaged, it is necessary to help him achieve self-independence. Dr. Rappaport says, "Relationship structure, a therapeutic approach carried into all facets of everyday living, is a catalyst which gives the other structures and techniques and devices the occasion to be effective. It is the tide which enables the child too long aground, because he lacked neurological intactness, to be launched in the direction of adequacy."[7]

Now let us visit still another well-known facility, one which provides both diagnostic and residential care on a broad continuum of service.

THE MENNINGER FOUNDATION

The Menninger Foundation has become a symbol of psychiatric concern. For more than forty years, when two members of the Menninger family formed a clinic, the Menninger name has been characteristic of diagnosis, treatment, and research into the fields of mental health and mental illness. The world knows of the work of Dr. Will C. Menninger, recently deceased, and his brother, Karl, and now of the good efforts of the next generation, Drs. Roy, Robert, and Philip Menninger.

One facet of the Menninger program will be considered here, that dealing with children, and especially with children who evidence disabilities in the area of learning. The story of Alice, whose nonlearning and whose fears about her father's health brought the family to the Menninger Foundation, has already been told in Chapter I. So has the philosophy

[7] *Ibid.*, p. 9.

of Dr. J. Cotter Hirschberg. Let us then look more generally at the program of the Menninger Foundation as it relates to children.

Here in Topeka, Kansas, one turns off the highway onto a smaller road set between a mile or more of rolling hills. Soft grass carpets large tree areas; brick buildings are far back from the road; and the impression gained is that this may be an entry to a country club rather than a hospital complex. Carefully tended flower beds border every building. The crisp air, the scent of growing bushes, the curving walks bespeak relaxation and warmth.

Each building in the children's complex houses doctors' offices, research rooms, residential areas, and recreation spots. Yet each is so constructed that it is separate from the other. Perhaps the physical buildings reflect the treatment program which gives the children room to grow into their own strengths yet with guidelines enough to know that professional help is close by. The Children's Division includes an outpatient service offering psychiatric, psychological, and neurological evaluation and treatment for children of all ages. The Children's Hospital, which is a residential treatment center for the admission of emotionally disturbed children between five and sixteen, completes the grouping.

Dr. Robert E. Switzer, who is director of the Children's Division, is a man who is busy, efficient, and accessible. A troubled youngster can barge into a conference without being reprimanded. A teacher or other professional worker can have almost instant access to Dr. Switzer for consultation.

A dark-eyed man with thinning hair, Dr. Switzer smiles quickly, and his face reflects the thousands of smiles which have crossed it. His office bears evidence of his feeling for children. There are art objects and pictures made by the youngsters. The room is filled with color.

The reception room itself is as inviting as the living room of a friend, and the staff gives the visitor the feeling of being a participant in a family get-together.

The team approach has been described. Dozens of specialties may be utilized in trying to diagnose one child during the ten-day evaluation. Fellows in training join the regular staff and learn as they work with children and their parents.

Let's visit several of these team members and see how they react to children with learning disabilities. Dr. Clyde Rousey, speech pathologist, tall, intense, echoes the words of others who work with these children with special problems. "To look at a speech problem as an entity in itself is misleading," he says. "It is a reflection of a learning disability. The child is the concern of the therapist, not the particular name put on his difficulty."

Dr. Rousey, who is associate professor of speech pathology at the University of Kansas as well as speech pathologist at the Menninger Foundation, feels that delayed speech may often be a symptom of interpersonal disturbance and thinks it vital that intervention procedures be introduced quite early for the child. He refutes the "wait and see" approach because he and his colleagues feel that much of the inhibition of speech in such a child is an effort to ward off anxiety. Immediate psychotherapeutic intervention for this condition is recommended rather than waiting for time to cure the problem.

As part of the Menninger team, Dr. Rousey sees most of the children who come through for diagnosis. The speech problem evidenced by them is put into the context of the other problems suffered by the child.

Another team member in the learning disability area is Dr. Phillip Rennick, who thinks that added efforts need to be made to work on something besides the deficit itself. He feels that we have underrated motivation and that if we described

Helen Keller's disability, we would never be able to predict the degree of her success. Without her motivation to learn despite the crippling disabilities, she would not have achieved the potential she did.

Dr. Rennick, tall, blue-eyed, intense, has a no-nonsense look about him when he talks of learning disabilities. "We should call them cognitive perceptual motor disabilities because that is what they are," he insists.

Perhaps the philosophy of the Menninger Foundation itself can be heard in the words often expressed by Dr. Dorothy Fuller, kindly and outgoing psychologist in the Children's Division. "God tempers the wind to the shorn lamb," she has said. "Here we try to shape the program to fit the child. However, the child must not resort to less adequate judgment than that of which he is capable."

The most dramatic case seen at the Menninger Foundation, according to Dr. Fuller, was that of a boy who had a high verbal ability but who functioned at a borderline level in all of his activities. He had had brain damage as an infant and was thought to be a borderline mental defective. Given a test in which he was supposed to draw a man, he could not even make a semblance of a human being. Slowly, painfully, carefully, Dr. Fuller aided him, along with the team, in sorting out his assets and liabilities.

He is now teaching in a college in the West and has completed two years toward his doctor's degree.

The severity of learning disability which strikes some children can be demonstrated in the case of Harvey, who will need to be in a protective environment for the remainder of his life. Nevertheless, he has learned enough about communication to be able to participate in activities with his peers and to read and enjoy many aspects of life.

Harvey stayed at the Menninger Foundation for almost

seven years. When he arrived, he was six years old and could not speak as well as a child of two and a half. Yet he could spell hippopotamus and rhinoceros and could write lists. It was impossible for Harvey to communicate directly with anyone. He strung words together, like beads on a string, but the listener had to follow the string, bead by bead, to get meaning. Finally he developed enough verbal and auditory symbols to be able to tell people what he wanted and needed. Sometimes he would take one of the Golden Book dictionaries, and the therapist would find out what he wanted to say by following the sequence of pictures to which he pointed. In order to say a word, he had to write it down first.

Harvey's learning disability has crippled him throughout life, but Harvey had the burden of emotional illness along with the slight symptoms of brain damage which was observable on examination.

What is school like at the Menninger Foundation? Since all of the children have crippling emotional problems in addition to their learning disorders, the emphasis is less on the techniques of learning per se and more on the whole structure of the classroom and the teachers in it. The same philosophy holds true at the Pathway School.

In order to learn about the schooling, let us go into the brick building housing the Southard School and talk with Randall Schmidt, the principal. Young and energetic, Mr. Schmidt looks like a football player. He is the kind of man who can symbolize strength to an acting-out youngster.

The school program goes from the first through the eleventh grade, and every child is expected to be in class for some portion of the day if he is able. All classes are ungraded, and the class sessions are highly structured.

What happens to a child who disrupts the class? He is taken by a child-care worker back to his residence hall. There he is required to do his schoolwork. Every child is expected to be able to learn and to function in school.

Randy Schmidt's blue eyes look directly at the listener as he says, "We expect children to learn and to be able to function in school. If he has not done an assignment, he either does it on the spot or deals with his problem right there. The teachers are not to be manipulated. We give a consistent frame of reference to the children. They know that we expect them to have successes."

Provision is made for those children who are so ill or so disorganized that they cannot tolerate a regular classroom. One highly structured unit is set up for vocational training. No anger is shown to the children who do not complete their work, but they know that they are expected to accomplish their task or to work on the problem which holds them back.

The Menninger children run the gamut, from those who can spend only an hour or two a day in any kind of learning situation to those who go to public schools in Topeka. Close rapport is maintained between the Menninger teachers and those in the public schools, and a social worker joins the team to work with school personnel, Menninger team, child, and parents.

School continues for eleven months of the year, and some of the young people are able to go on to college.

What about children who have definite learning problems which are observable? According to Mr. Schmidt, they receive close individual instruction, utilizing the various methods known for teaching reading skills.

The school building contains a large airy, colorful library. Here young people are free to browse and to select reading for pleasure or for schoolwork.

In a room behind the library, groups of youngsters meet at regularly scheduled intervals for council sessions with Miss

Mary Jane Baxter, a social worker. What looks like a simple club for young people is, in reality, an important part of the therapy program. In residential treatment the young people interact frequently with adults—in psychotherapy, social case-work, and classrooms. Since much time is spent in the group, peer relationships often uncover stresses. The council is used as an extra means of understanding and helping the child.

Council members are selected from the five separate living units with children in residence. Since the ages on admission range from five and a half to seventeen, many kinds of prob-lems can emerge. Weekly house meetings provide the agenda for the council sessions. Nominees for participation have to be approved by the residential psychiatrist.

The aim is to improve the social functioning of the chil-dren. According to Miss Baxter, "The process of council in-volves consideration of solutions, demands, testing, and after some trials, healthy responses. In this sense it affords oppor-tunity for more mature experiences and is ego strengthening."

The dynamics of the council may not be apparent to the casual visitor, who sees five impatient young people, from pre-adolescent to late teens, arguing among themselves over what movies are to be shown to the group. Yet, according to Miss Baxter, whose specialty is group work, such self-government allows the children to work together to find socially acceptable and satisfying solutions to their everyday problems.

There is tall, awkward Julie, whose protruding brace frame makes her look like some creature from outer space. And lanky Morris, bad-skinned and bad-tempered. Chubby Harry, the chairman, has the look of a sculptured cherub. Not so, Paul, a compulsive talker, high-voiced, bright, and unappealing-looking with his long hair and thick glasses. And then there is Frieda, a pretty girl who spends most of her time biting her nails.

Anger is quick to rise in these sessions, and there is little tolerance for frustration. The young people seem to have small ability to interact. Disturbances run like a heavy river beneath the hard surface ice. One heavy step, and the group falls in with a splash.

In addition to regular schooling, the children at Menninger's also have therapeutic living quarters. A central living room contains television and games, and the individual sleeping rooms are filled with personal symbols of identity. Brewster, whose father heads a large corporation, fills his walls with pictures of the family estate and the boats he has owned. A short-wave radio and expensive games are well displayed. Yet for Brewster the program is identical with that for Fred, who was sent by the county and whose room is sparsely decorated.

Occupational therapy is part of the program. Here again a child's quick frustration and anger are dealt with on the spot by the therapist, who remains supportive, calm, and helpful. A broken tile may be flung across the room. The youngster who threw it will not be scolded, but he will be expected to pick up the pieces and to discuss the anger which lay behind the throwing episode.

Janie, whose heavy glasses keep falling down her nose, sands a block of wood. But her hand falters and slips. Before her quick anger can rise, the therapist takes her hand and says gently, "Go with the grain." Janie stands immobilized, and the therapist takes her hand and works with her, saying softly, "Are you with me? Where are your eyes?", forcing Janie to return to the relationship between them.

George works at putting a wire on the back of a picture. The therapist shows him the way, and George tries again. The wire gets twisted, and again the fast anger begins to rise. The therapist takes his hand. "All right," George screams. "All right."

The therapist is endlessly patient and very quiet. She helps each child to develop both skill and tolerance. Everything at the Menninger program is designed to shore up the ego strengths of the children and to help them cope with life.

For the child with serious problems in learning, the evaluation process can help to pinpoint the areas of difficulty. For the child whose learning process has been halted or delayed by a large overlay of emotional difficulties, some long-term help may be needed.

† † †

We have looked at two programs of residential care for children with severe difficulties and have seen that in both the team members are like a resource bank of strength from which the children can borrow to shore up their own weak and faltering egos. Frank knows that a catastrophic collapse will be understood, that he will be helped to his feet physically and psychologically, and that he will be given the chance to try again at his own level and his own speed. Paul recognizes that the council members and the social workers will stop him from exceeding the bounds of monopolizing the group and trying to turn them to his way of thinking.

In these programs the agony of the children themselves is recognized but not catered to. The unbearable frustration felt by a child who cannot throw a ball or read a line or subtract a simple number sequence is felt to some degree by each person working with the children. The swift anger expressed is dealt with, but not with answering anger. Rather, the feeling given the children by the professional is that of "I am strong, and I will help you to become strong too. I will lend you my strength as long as you need it, but you must work to develop skills and abilities of your own."

"The wind is tempered to the shorn lamb." The children know that the clipped quality of their functioning is known and accepted, that there will be gentle breezes of acceptance and the warm sun of strength to help them grow to their own capacities.

The four programs viewed are geared to children with serious difficulties in learning and language. It would have been possible to crisscross the country and to see a hundred other operations. Some of them are university-connected and are part of research institutes. Others are privately supported and are beamed toward a specific area of disability, such as reading. Some of them use a definite method to reach children; others utilize a combination of skills. There are institutes primarily for teaching, residential centers for full-time therapy, programs to work on the disability itself several hours a week.

The programs differ greatly. So do the children. We have looked at youngsters who were able to hide their disability from the world; others who were unable to cope with any day in their lives.

Where is the common denominator in the programs and in the children? For the youngsters themselves the ability to communicate, to reach others, and to be able to exist in an orderly fashion in an uncertain world is their great need.

The ingredient which these four facilities and all good centers have in common is that of dedicated concern. The persons working with the young people seem to let their own ego strength flow into the arid cups of self which these children hold. They exude a patient strength which lets the children know that here their brokenness can be seen and can be put together.

In the next chapter we shall look at legislative efforts which are being made on behalf of children with learning problems. Some possible sources of reference for parents of such youngsters will be reviewed. No simple answer will or can be given.

CHAPTER V

CONCLUSION
"Whose Responsibility?"

HERE THEY ARE. An army of children. Some of them still infants fighting phantoms in their cribs. Others have grown into adulthood, stumbling through a disordered world. Many are now in school, tasting the sour fruit of failure.

Here they are. John and solid Kim. Marty, Alice, and Polly. Pretty Sherry and frightened Bruce. Butch, Marcy, Frank—Fred, Carolyn, and Nicky. Keith and Don and the hundreds and thousands of other children whose world is tilted, uncertain, or totally upside down. A sad army of young people on a treasure hunt without a map.

Some of them are so disordered that their disruption has caused action by parents or by teachers. Others are vaguely troubled, uncertain, afraid. They may withdraw from the hurt of learning situations, and their withdrawal may cause a mingling of academic and emotional problems. They may thrash about in an uncertain world, and their thrashing may bring them into trouble with the law. They may stumble through life in vague, disordered fashion, without accomplishment or satisfaction.

Whose responsibility are these people? Their parents'? Anyone else's? Is Kim a part of the community, as much as Hardy, who won a football scholarship to the state university? Is Polly a member of the town to the same extent as Hilda, who married that wonderful doctor and moved to a mansion on the hill?

How quick the community is to claim the achievers. How equally fast it disclaims the lawbreakers and the problem

149

bearers. Yet towns and cities are composed of a mosaic of people, all of whom constitute the total community.

Whose responsibility? Whose responsibility is Eula May? Isabel? They live near the city dump with their mothers, who clean houses for a living. Yet Eula May and Isabel will be part of the same school system as Hilda's children and may need an inordinate amount of special services unless attention is given them now. The community has the basic problem. The better prepared the child is for living, the better neighbor he becomes.

The renewed awareness of community responsibility for all of its people is reflected in national, statewide, and local programs for comprehensive mental health services of all kinds. Some problems can be prevented. Others have progressed to a point where intervention becomes necessary; still others must receive specialized treatment.

Many ways of preventing brain injury before birth are being learned. The expectant mother's health, her drug intake, and her travel plans are all studied by the alert obstetrician. During delivery the kinds and amounts of analgesic drugs used are evaluated in order to effect prompt respiration of infants. Newborn babies who have such difficulties benefit from improved treatment with oxygen and resuscitation. Many possible cases of brain injury caused by prolonged high temperatures in children are being prevented by prompt methods of treating infections and reducing temperatures.

Physicians are campaigning also for methods to keep infants from avoidable falls. Many cases of brain injury in children are thought to be caused by early spills from cribs, high chairs, or beds resulting in head blows to the infant.

All of these preventive methods may help to reduce the numbers of children who suffer from observable brain injury and possibly from various kinds of minimal brain dysfunction.

Children with learning disorders can benefit most from very early intervention procedures. Such youngsters can be spotted at young ages and given help before the problem has swelled into large and complicated proportions. A sometimes confusing multitude of treatment programs also exists.

Every parent wishes his child to have the finest tools to serve him throughout life. No mother or father wants a youngster to wash clothes on the riverbank with stones when everyone else has automatic washing machines. No parent would stand his child up with a slingshot against an enemy with a gun. To acquire the tools with which to shape an adequate life in today's society requires multiple learning skills.

What, then, are the ways in which parents, physicians, teachers, and other professional personnel can work together toward the singular goal of helping the child with learning disabilities? Is the problem really great enough to merit the concern of people everywhere? In this day of gigantic numbers, it is easy to become inured to multiple thousands. However, 3,000,000 children comprise a sizable population. And that is how many children with specific learning disabilities there may be by 1975.

The figure comes from Dr. Wayne Sengstock, of the National Association for Retarded Children, who testified before the Ad Hoc Committee on the Handicapped, as follows: "It is predicted that by 1975 there will be 75 million children in our school-age population. Of these 12 million will be handicapped. Within this . . . population, it is estimated that there will be some 3,000,000 mentally retarded . . . and another 3,000,000 with specific learning disability which will represent a functional retardation unless strategic special intervention takes place."[1]

[1] Association for Children with Learning Disabilities, Tulsa, Oklahoma: Special Report on Legislation and Learning Disabilities.

Bill Barclay, at the age of almost six years, was one of the fortunate ones because there was a Dr. Howard in Central. However, Bill may be unlike some other child with brain injury or another kind of brain dysfunction. Dr. Samuel Kirk, appearing before a Senate Subcommittee on Education, talked of the many facets of learning and the ways in which various children may be affected. He illustrated his statement by discussing three different children. One boy could not recognize objects. Three ophthalmologists had examined him and declared him to have normal vision, but he could not even recognize the children with whom he came in contact. Another child could not differentiate or discriminate tones, although hearing tests had shown him to have normal hearing sensitivity. The spoken word meant nothing to him. Still another child could not read, but he was of normal general intelligence.

No child is exactly like Bill Barclay; yet all of the children with learning disabilities share in common the need for specialized training and for programs which can help them grow into adulthood in as productive a manner as possible. Children like Bill need help on many fronts. They need it medically, educationally, psychologically, and legislatively. Such aid has to come through the multiple efforts of many people in communities, and through them in state and national programs.

Recommendations have been made on behalf of this large population of youngsters who often falter through life wearing the disguises of whole people and bearing the pain of brokenness. What has happened legislatively?

Legislature Programs

To find out, questions were directed to Paul Ackerman, of the National Education Association and director of its Study of State Legislation for the Council for Exceptional Children.

In making his report for the Task Force on Learning Disabilities of the U.S. Office of Education, Mr. Ackerman pointed out that legislation does not always reflect a state's commitment to special education programs. Sometimes the legislation is enabling, providing legal authority for a governing board, a state director of special education, or a local school board to set up policies for such education programs. In other states, the administrative body is restricted by laws which define, include, and exclude programs for certain disabled children. Mr. Ackerman points out that his report only delineates the legal structure whereby states may or may not expand their programs in the area. He also states that in order to see what plans may be ongoing on behalf of learning disordered children, it is necessary to know all of the statutes on the books. As an example, vocational rehabilitation legislation may augment special education legislation and services provided to children.

Four categories of legislation emerged from the study:

1. In some legislation, exceptional children statutes excluded programs which might be conducive to remediation of learning disabilities.
2. Other legislation included a category of learning disabilities, although interpretation of the concept was seemingly not made.
3. In some states legislation was favorable to operations for remediation of learning disabilities. In those instances, programs could be instituted with simply minor changes in the statutes.
4. The category of learning disability, brain dysfunction, or severe learning disabilities appeared in the statutes of several states.

The first category is inclusive of 17 states. Legislation here either bars learning disabilities by explaining carefully what handicaps can be served or by definitions which exclude children who have less intellectual impairment than that which is legally defined. In these instances legislation would have to be changed to bring about innovative programs.

The second category encompasses 13 states which could provide programs for children with learning disabilities. In these states legislation is broad, and learning disabilities, while not mentioned specifically, could be included if the legislation is interpreted broadly. Although a number of these states define three or four other disability categories and in this way limit possible services, they do provide room for expansion of services.

In the third instance, eight states seem to favor providing special education for children with learning disabilities, although they do not name the category specifically. Other names such as "slow learner" or "aphasic" or even "miscellaneous" are employed but might be used to give special education services to those children who have serious learning disabilities.

Finally, six states have statutes which include the term "learning disabilities" or something similar in the legislation. They are California, Colorado, Connecticut, Idaho, New York, and Oregon. In most instances such provision has been made through pilot programs which are designed to demonstrate what might be done for this special population of children.

Four comments made by Mr. Ackerman reflect the possibilities of state movement on behalf of the learning-disabled children.

1. He suggests that vocational rehabilitation legislation in every state should be examined. In many instances it can be directed toward the child with learning disability.

2. Permanent planning committees have been established in a few states. In Florida, a commission has been set up to help plan and execute future legislation. Other states have only advisory or temporary planning commissions.
3. In some instances federal legislation will be useless unless the state legislation is changed.
4. Several states, including Oklahoma and Texas, have undertaken special studies to initiate programs in learning disabilities.

Thus, it can be seen that steps are being taken.

Recommendations

Six recommendations were made by the president of the Association for Children with Learning Disabilities, before the Ad Hoc Committee on the Handicapped of the Committee on Education and Labor, U.S. House of Representatives.[2]

The first of these had to do with the training and use of child development specialists. Such specialists could be used in the early grades of school to help in assessing and programming needs of these children. Educational therapy could be provided during set times of the day for those youngsters needing it. For the children requiring special classes, small ones could be provided, utilizing regular classroom teachers under the supervision of the child development specialists. Such specialists would serve in still another capacity, that of resources to the parents. As Meg Barclay discovered from Dr. Howard, the home treatment of the child with serious learning disabilities is an important part of his overall program. Because the child's abilities and disabilities vary from time to time and because a continuing and ever-changing program of

[2] *Ibid.,* pp. 15, 16.

therapy is needed, the parents can use the knowledge and suggestions of specialists who are trained to spot and to help ameliorate problems arising in the handling of such children.

The second suggestion concerned the social and recreational needs of the children whose learning patterns are different from those of the majority of youngsters. Planned recreation in camps and community programs can help those children with special learning or speech problems to have the experiences which so-called normal young people enjoy. The professional personnel working in a recreational setting with these youngsters also gain special insights from the daily and hourly contact with them.

The third recommendation dealt with the availability of special educational materials. The child with learning disabilities needs a variety of possible books, games, programmed materials, and films in order to develop. Teachers of such children should have the benefit of well-designed and well-planned materials which can aid them in their teaching programs.

A fourth idea concerned vocational training. Not all children can benefit from school programs which include reading and mathematics. Some are helped too late; others are so retarded in reading ability that they cannot catch up with the ordinary school population. For those young people who cannot progress to college or to business schools, special help needs to be given in vocational assessment and training. Community agencies, if properly funded, can help with developing such young people into careers in which they can fit and be productive.

The fifth recommendation proposed having funds earmarked for the purpose of giving special education and services to the children with learning disabilities. In the past it has been necessary for many groups of parents to band together to form private schools which their children could attend.

The sixth recommendation made was that learning disabilities become a category in legislation. The creation of some kind of organization to establish a national policy and plan for meeting the needs of learning-disabled children and youth would be helpful. The problems of this special population of children would then become visible. It was suggested that such an organization might fall within the province of the Department of Health, Education, and Welfare.

Bureau of Education for the Handicapped

This recommendation became reality late in 1967 when a Bureau of Education for the Handicapped was formed under the aegis of the Office of Education of the Department of Health, Education, and Welfare. The bureau is charged with stimulating research, training, and services for all kinds of handicapped children.

Three major divisions exist under the bureau. One of them is the Division of Research, the major mission of which is to discover new knowledge and to investigate effective ways of organizing and disseminating educational knowledge in all areas of the handicapped. The purpose of a second division, the Division of Training Programs, is to support and provide leadership for training institutions in their efforts to produce skilled personnel so that the best of current professional practices are brought to as many handicapped children as possible. One branch of this division is the Communication Disorders Branch, and another is the Special Learning Problems Branch.

A third major area is the Division of Educational Services, charged with providing special resources to local, state, and regional programs, assisting their development of the best of current practices in the field of special education. The many responsibilities of the division fall into three major categories which form the basis for branches. Under the Aid to States Branch are two major sections representing different legislative authorities. The first section administers the grants-to-states program of Title VI of the Elementary and Secondary Education Act. The second edition administers the aid to state-operated or -supported institutions under P.L. 89-313. This program is designed to bring effective educational procedures to severely handicapped children.

Appropriations for fiscal 1968 consisted of $53,400,000 for educational improvement for the handicapped. It was divided into $11,100,000 for research; $24,500,000 for training of professional personnel; $2,800,000 for media services and captioned films for the deaf; and $15,000,000 for Title VI, Elementary and Secondary Education Act.

In addition, an estimated $15 to $24 million of the total appropriation for Title I, Elementary and Secondary Education Act, was earmarked for the Public Law 89-313 program of support to the states for state-operated and state-supported schools for the handicapped. The total program for the Bureau of Education for the Handicapped for fiscal 1968, then, came to between $68.4 to $77.4 million.

†   †   †

The spotlight of recognition shines on the child with serious learning disabilities. In increasing numbers pediatricians, psychologists, parents, educators, and legislators are joining hands in mutual effort to provide services for children who have handicaps often serious and unseen, undertows in the waters of their lives.

The roles of the pediatrician, the psychologist, the educator, the family members, and the legislator have all been examined. Each of them has a unique and vital role to play in helping the child with learning disabilities. Each of them needs to demonstrate a willingness to work with the other disciplines in setting out program and goals for the learning-disabled child.

Research

Because the problem is not one problem but many, because manifestations of difficulties appear in many guises, because solutions must be multiple, research efforts need to be increased. Only through concentrated research will workers be able to build on actual evidence and methods. Currently research is going on in medical schools, universities, and school classrooms. A sampling of some of the research follows.

Numerous studies are emerging with support by the National Institute of Mental Health. Included in the subjects being surveyed are the processes by which the child learns basic intellectual and perceptual skills. Without such knowledge, it is impossible to understand what goes on in the "damaged" child, the learning-disabled, the mentally retarded, or the emotionally disturbed. Classroom management techniques are also subjects for investigation. Specifically, two NIMH-supported investigators are trying to find better ways of diagnosing and treating aphasia and of understanding the use of language. Several studies of learning concern themselves with the effect of social reinforcement or reward on a child's response to learning tasks.[3]

One of the most important of the Institute-supported programs aims at developing procedures for detecting and remedying ineffective functioning in the primary school child. This study deals with emotionally disturbed and normal chil-

[3] *Mental Health of Children.* Bethesda, Maryland: Public Health Service Publication No. 1396, December 1965, pp. 17–22.

dren at kindergarten through first-grade level in five public schools. Here teacher-aides, volunteer housewives, give personal attention and academic and emotional support to the children.

Recognizing that shortage of manpower becomes a critical factor in any program of study or research, the National Institute of Mental Health funds numerous training grants in psychiatry, psychology, social work, nursing, and social sciences.

Other government agencies sponsor programs of research in order to help increase knowledge and competencies in many fields. The Veterans Administration is one such sponsor. In California a study of memory, another on the brain cycle of sleeping and waking, and a third on cerebral anoxia, a study which might have a direct bearing on brain injury and its attendant learning problems, are being undertaken.[4]

Some of the research occurs right in the classroom. Systematic recording of events or sequences of events provides a major research format in special education. The research effort comes in ordering and correlating the information gathered into a meaningful whole. Perhaps Dr. Eli Bower of the National Institute of Mental Health leads the list of the researchers doing school screening for adjustment vulnerability.

In many of the programs described in this book studies are underway on various aspects of learning disabilities in the population of children. Hundreds of studies are in various stages of completion, from minute and detailed psychological brain studies to observations on gross populations of children. Although they vary in size and intensity, all of them add to the body of knowledge which is needed before consistent help can be given to children who have learning problems.

[4] *Psychiatric Research in the Veterans Administration.* Washington, D.C.: VA Pamphlet 10-78, pp. 14–16.

To demonstrate how important a varied approach is for aiding children who have brain injury or serious learning problems, two professors from the Yale University School of Medicine and Child Study Center discussed their work with a group of children referred to the clinic.[5]

The children who were involved in this particular experiment ranged from educable to superior in intelligence. Many, but not all, of them showed the behavioral systems typical of many brain-injured children, hyperactivity, distractibility, and emotional instability. School adjustment was difficult for all of them, and each one presented problems of behavior which made life at home difficult for everyone.

After several years of working with children who suffered such impairments, the professional team concluded that the work with parents and school was quite essential, but equally important was the familiarity which the therapist had with the community's resources, organizations, and individuals. "We have effectively recommended a large range of educational and social experiences in order to promote the balanced development of the child's assets and liabilities."[6]

It is pointed out that assessment of the handicapped child's ego strengths and deficits is crucial for helping the child to adapt to his environment. "Treatment is tailored by knowing more accurately what such children need and which sectors of adaptation can be strengthened through treatment, education, and guided experiences in the home and community."[7]

A comprehensive program of treatment for the child with learning disabilities demonstrates the multiplicity of ap-

[5] John Doris and Albert J. Solnit, "Treatment of Children with Brain Damage and Associated School Problems," *Journal of American Child Psychiatry,* Vol. 2, No. 4, October 1963, pp. 618–635.

[6] *Ibid.,* pp. 630–631.

[7] *Ibid.,* p. 631.

proaches and the variety of methods which are needed to help the child develop his strengths and overcome his disabilities.

Information and Activities

Parents of the nonlearning child hunger for information. When they recognize that their son or daughter has a disability, they generally are eager to read about the problem and to learn what groups are doing. Teachers, other professional persons, and concerned citizens also express interest in increasing their understanding of problems such as those presented by children with learning disabilities.

To answer the needs of such groups, the *Journal of Learning Disabilities* began publication in January of 1968. Purpose of the *Journal* is stated as being "for the many involved professional disciplines, the classroom teachers, and knowledgeable lay persons."[8] The editors go on to say, "The pages of the *Journal* will offer an open forum for everyone concerned . . . the diversity may be startling . . . the objectives will always be the same—to explore and report every responsible approach to mastering the problems that are frustrating so many children and adults throughout the world."

Another journal devoting itself to the cause of children with special problems is *Exceptional Children,* a publication of the Council for Exceptional Children.

A new division of the Council came into being in 1967 when persons interested in its formation within the Council made known their desire. From an open forum held during the 45th Council for Exceptional Children Convention, plans were made for an organizational meeting of a Division for Children with Learning Disabilities. Membership is open to all

[8] "Statement of Purpose," *Journal of Learning Disabilities,* Chicago, Illinois: Martin Topaz, p. 58.

members of C.E.C. who are interested in the welfare and education of children with learning disabilities.

Still another publication concerned with human disabilities, many of them in children, is the publication of the National Society for Crippled Children and Adults, *Rehabilitation Literature*.

Parents have provided the impetus for one of the fastest-growing movements in the area of learning disabilities in children. The concern of the mothers and fathers of children who had difficulties prompted the initiation of an Association for Children with Learning Disabilities. The fifth international conference was held in February of 1968 in Boston. Discussions during the three-day conference centered on medical aspects of the problem, teacher participation, legislation, the problems of both preschoolers and adolescents, parental roles, and educational programs available. Many states have affiliated chapters.

Whose Responsibility?

But parents do not or should not face the problem entirely alone.

The difficulties have been seen scientifically by the medical profession, educators, behavioral scientists. Parents have been both baffled and supportive. Programs have been instituted.

But has enough been done? Is enough being done? That answer has to be given by each individual whose general concern is for the well-being of people everywhere and at all times. Everyone knows the circularity of failure and of poverty. Poor families beget other poor families who beget still more. Unless the cycle is broken, unless new skills and abilities are taught, the dragline of poverty pulls constantly at those persons in the slum areas.

So it is with childhood problems. The child who is a

failure—David, "dull," "stupid," or nonachieving Joel—how can they perceive life and people? And if they marry, what can they give to their children but a plodding sense of failure and inadequacy? The summary statement from the report of the National Institute of Mental Health states the problem thus:

> In the final analysis, the mental health of our children hinges on the maturity and health of our society—from the smallest unit to the largest. The structure of the home and the wellbeing of the family, the compassion of the surrounding community, the social conscience and social action of our government and its citizens—all of these are crucial. If we fail at any point, the outcome is clear: the hurt child grows to hurt his own children and—despite heroic individual efforts—we walk an inexorable treadmill of pathology and pain.[9]

"In the final analysis, the mental health of our children hinges on the maturity and health of our society . . ." Dr. Darrel Mase has stated that it is his belief that no group should ever get together on any matter for any action until they have first had a "picnic." When they have had a picnic, he says, and have discovered that they all like the same kind of milk or something, it is very possible that they may then be able to communicate . . .[10]

And this communication between disciplines, between parent and professional worker, between child and "others," is the vital chemical which can synthesize all of the individual efforts and bring oneness from diversity.

Increasingly, in this era, the well-being of children, all

[9] *Mental Health of Children, op. cit.,* p. 59.

[10] Darrel J. Mase, Dean, College of Health Related Professions, The J. Hillis Miller Health Center, University of Florida, Gainesville, Florida. Talk on "Straightening Crooked Paths," Second Annual Meeting, Association for Children with Learning Disabilities, May 1965.

children, concerns us. We ache with the hunger of an Indian toddler; we hurt with the pain of a wounded Vietnamese youngster; we suffer for the slum child. For we know, know deeply, that every child belongs to us and that no child is ours alone.

We know of the child with learning disabilities. We feel his vague hunger for a food he has never tasted—and we recognize his sense of self-blame that he has not eaten.

His days are days of shadows, and he knows no sun. The fog lifts from time to time, showing him a bit of the world or a piece of life, tantalizing as a veiled woman who reveals only a portion of her mystery.

He walks through a forest of huge and rough-barked trees. There is an occasional path which he can follow, but it often ends without taking him to the clearing. There is no guide, and he stumbles.

He is like the small boy who was lifted from the ground by a tornado. As he whirled within the cylinder of the storm, he saw birds and bits of wood, leaves from trees, and debris twirling with him in a frenzied cycle which held him in its power.

It matters not what we call him. A child with learning disabilities. Or one with minimal brain dysfunction. A perceptually handicapped child. Or a brain-damaged one. Kim or Alice. Polly. Frank, Ted. Joel or Timmy.

What we call him is but a tag. What we see and feel about him prompts action.

He is a child who knows he is different. He is a child who "cannot," while other children "can." He may live in a kaleidoscopic world of twirling lights and pieces. He knows a pain too deep for crying. He is a kite without a string. His world comes in pieces, like a gigantic puzzle he cannot solve. It tilts; it fragments; it turns completely upside-down.

Steady hands are needed. Many hands lifting, turning, working together on behalf of this bewildered child . . . working to bring life into focus and to right for him this world of upside-down.

SOURCES OF INFORMATION

Some Journals Concerning Learning Disabilities

Academic Therapy Quarterly, published each season by the DeWitt Reading Clinic, Inc., 1543 Fifth Avenue, San Rafael, California 94901 (for persons in educational, medical, psychological fields working with children and adolescents).

Exceptional Children, A Journal of the Council for Exceptional Children, 1201 Sixteenth Street, N.W., Washington, D.C. 20005.

Journal of Educational Research, Dembar Educational Research Services, Inc., Box 1605, Madison, Wisconsin 53701.

Journal of Learning Disabilities, The Professional Press, Inc., Room 1410, 5 North Wabash Avenue, Chicago, Illinois 60602.

Language Learning, A Journal of Applied Linguistics, North University Building, Ann Arbor, Michigan 48107.

† † †

Some Places Where Information May Be Obtained

Association for Children with Learning Disabilities, Inc., 3739 South Delaware Place, Tulsa, Oklahoma 74105.

Council for Exceptional Children, Division for Children with Learning Disabilities, a Department of the National Education Association, P.O. Box 9382 Mid City Station, Washington, D.C. 20005.

Division of Training Programs, Bureau of Education for the Handicapped, U.S. Office of Education, 400 Maryland Avenue, S.W., Washington, D.C. 20202.

National Institute for Mental Health, 5454 Wisconsin Avenue, Chevy Chase, Maryland 20203.

National Institute of Neurological Diseases and Blindness, a department of the National Department of Health, Bethesda, Maryland 20202.

National Society for Crippled Children and Adults, Inc., 2023 West Ogden Avenue, Chicago, Illinois 60612.

† † †

Some Proceedings, Bibliography, Monographs About Learning Disorders

Educational Management of Children with Learning Disabilities (Indexed Bibliography), Ruth Edgington and Sam D. Clements, Argus Communications, 3505 N. Ashland Avenue, Chicago, Illinois 60657.

International Approach to Learning Disabilities of Children and Youth (Selected Conference Papers, 1967), The Association for Children with Learning Disabilities, Inc., 3739 South Delaware Place, Tulsa, Oklahoma 74105.

Learning and Its Disorders, Volume 1, Edited by I. N. Berlin, M.D., and S. A. Szurek, M.D., Science and Behavior Books, Inc., 577 College Avenue, Palo Alto, California 94306.

Learning Disorders, Volume 1, Edited by Jerome Hellmuth, 1965, Special Child Publications of the Seattle Seguin School, Inc., 71 Columbia Street, Seattle, Washington 98104.

Proceedings of Convocation on Children and Young Adults with Learning Disabilities, Mafex Associates, Inc., Box 519, Johnstown, Pennsylvania 15907.

Proceedings of the Second Colloquium on Exceptional Chil-

dren and Youth, 1966, The University of Texas, College of Education, Austin, Texas 78712.

Rehabilitation Literature, National Society for Crippled Children and Adults, Inc., 2023 West Ogden Avenue, Chicago, Illinois 60612.

INDEX